A Book of

Great Worth

DAVE MARGOSHES

A Book of

Great Worth

Coteau Books

Edited by Geoffrey Ursell
Cover designed by David Drummond
Typeset by Susan Buck
Printed and bound in Canada   10 9 8 7 6 5 4 3 2 1

Library and Archives Canada Cataloguing in Publication

Margoshes, Dave, 1941-
    A book of great worth / Dave Margoshes.

Issued also in an electronic format.
ISBN 978-1-55050-476-7

    I. Title.

PS8576.A647B66 2012   C813'.54   C2011-908477-5

Library and Archives Canada Cataloguing in Publication

Margoshes, Dave, 1941-
    A book of great worth [electronic resource] / Dave Margoshes.

Electronic monograph in EPUB format.
Issued also in print format.
ISBN 978-1-55050-704-1

    I. Title.

PS8576.A647B66 2012   C813'.54   C2011-908478-3

COTEAU
BOOKS

2517 Victoria Avenue
Regina, Saskatchewan
Canada   S4P 0T2
www.coteaubooks.com

Available in Canada from:
Publishers Group Canada
2440 Viking Way
Richmond, British Columbia
Canada   V6V 1N2

Coteau Books gratefully acknowledges the financial support of its publishing program by: the Saskatchewan Arts Board, the Canada Council for the Arts, the Government of Canada through the Canada Book Fund, the Government of Saskatchewan through the Creative Economy Entrepreneurial Fund and the City of Regina Arts Commission.

This book is dedicated to the memory of my father,
Harry Margoshes (also known as Morgenstern),
1893–1975

About the sketch on previous page

Harry Margoshes, at his desk at *The Day* sometime in the Nineteen Forties, as depicted by the paper's editorial cartoonist, painter Josef Foshko.

Contents

The Proposition

"I did something stupid," the rabbi told my father.

It was 1925, New York City, a bar on the Lower East Side.

My father was a few years away from marriage, fatherhood, respectability, and so was prone to do stupid things himself: stay up late, associate with rough customers, drink too much, sing off-key – which really was the only way my father knew how to sing. But a rabbi doing a stupid thing? And not just any rabbi, but his good friend Lev Bronstyn, who was more like a big brother to him than any of his own big brothers were.

"I'm not joking, Harry," Bronstyn said. "I mean really stupid." He took a sip of whisky. "It involves a woman."

"Ah," my father said.

"It's bad, Harry," the rabbi said. Bronstyn had a long, often damp nose and prominent ears, which combined to make his head appear larger than normal. He shook it now. "Very bad."

My father was not a religious man, but he lived in a religious world. Sometimes those two forces – one pro, the other not necessarily anti but neutral – came together in a powerful, even violent clash.

More than three million Jews lived in the New York

City of the Twenties and Thirties, more than the total population of some states, and the Lower East Side, where my father worked, was their capital. Many of them, if not most, were religious, at least to the extent that they believed in God, went to *shul*, kept kosher, honoured and sought the counsel of rabbis. My father did none of these but he didn't make a show of it. He was a Jew, he thought, but not Jewish, a fine distinction.

He was, by his own reckoning, a socialist, a humanist, an autodidact, and, to the extent that he could be, a freethinker and an intellectual. The religious instruction he'd had as a child in Galicia, in Eastern Europe, had come to naught – after the family moved to America, around the turn of the century, interest in religion had waned for all but my grandmother who remained devout until her death, and my father was working as a blacksmith's helper at a stable on the Bowery on his thirteenth birthday and never did have his *bar mitzvah*. That was a loss his mother, my *bubba*, regretted, but he didn't.

By the time he began to write for *Der Tag* or *The Day*, all thoughts of religion were far behind him, although the newspaper conveyed a conservative slant that appealed to religious elements in the Jewish community. Soon he began to cover labour and was frequenting the Café Royale on Second Avenue and the Garden Cafeteria, just down the street from *The Day* building, hanging around with poets and playwrights, socialists, communists and anarchists, people who had no use for religion.

So it was a little strange that one of my father's best friends during this period of his life was a rabbi.

Dave Margoshes

Bronstyn called on my father at *The Day*'s offices at 187 East Broadway one Monday around noon and they walked the block and a half to a tavern on Henry Street where they could have a lunch for just a nickel extra with a beer. It was too crowded and noisy to talk but my father could tell something was on Bronstyn's mind. After a while, when the crowd had thinned somewhat, they bought shots of whisky and moved to the booth at the end of a long row of them.

"I did something stupid," Bronstyn began.

"It's about time," my father said, smiling. "You're altogether too smart for your own good."

"I'm not joking, Harry," Bronstyn said. "I mean really stupid. This is bad."

"What could be so bad?"

"It involves a woman." He took a handkerchief from his jacket pocket and wiped his nose.

"Ah," my father said. He was still a young man, with relatively little personal experience with women, although he'd had a bittersweet romance in Cleveland a few years earlier. But he was a keen student of human nature, and he'd observed that when men were in trouble it almost always involved a woman, to some extent at least. His stint as an advice columnist in Cleveland had certainly confirmed that.

Bronstyn was frowning at his drink, silent, and after a minute my father nodded his head and asked, "Surely not one of the women from those houses?"

"Yes," Bronstyn said.

Immediately, my father gave his full attention to his friend.

Bronstyn, on completion of his theological studies, had declined a position as a working rabbi. Instead, he had pursued a career in social work, and was now employed at a large Jewish agency that gave assistance of various sorts to orphans, unwed mothers, battered and otherwise abused women and children, and people of both sexes dealing with the deleterious effects of poverty. White slavery, the term applied to the mixture of sweet talk and intimidation used to coerce women, mostly right off the boat from Europe, into prostitution, was an especially serious problem on the Lower East Side, where dozens, perhaps hundreds, of brothels thrived, catering to lonely immigrants separated from their families. Bronstyn, who was affectionately known to his co-workers as "the rabbi," headed up a small unit dedicated to saving women from prostitution.

This was of interest to my father, who, as a young reporter eager to make a name for himself, was always on the lookout for a good story. He wrote several feature stories on the white-slavery problem, and, that April, soon after Passover, he was invited along on a number of raids coordinated between Bronstyn's agency and the police on brothels believed to be holding Jewish women against their will. His stories about these raids, accompanied by photographs, were splashed across the front page of the usually restrained *Day* and caused a sensation throughout the Lower East Side and the city in general, where the Jewish community had preferred to look the other way. A story my father wrote, based on interviews with some of the freed women, and headlined "Someone's daughters," was especially controversial, and was a feather in his cap. He was grateful to Bronstyn for having steered him to these stories and helped him get them, while Bronstyn, in turn, was grateful to my father for publicizing the problem and his agency's efforts.

Most recently, my father had written a story detailing how Bronstyn's agency was trying to help the women re-establish normal lives, finding them places to live and jobs, helping to locate family members, providing English lessons. He knew that Bronstyn and his colleagues worked closely with the women, in order to gain their trust.

Bronstyn took a tentative sip of his whisky. "I was careless," he said. "Reckless."

He explained that following the most recent raid he had become unnecessarily close to one particular woman who had opened up to him with her problems and fears. He had taken a personal interest in her case.

"This woman, she's attractive?" My father asked. It wasn't a disingenuous question, as he knew that many of the prostitutes, despite their youth and the life they'd been forced into, were plain.

"Very," Bronstyn said. His normal hangdog expression was exaggerated, and the length of his already long face, from brow to chin, seemed to grow even as my father watched him. Again, he wiped at his nose with his handkerchief. "But it isn't what you may think, believe me Harry. Nothing happened. I was reckless, stupid, yes, but…"

"If nothing happened, then nothing happened," my father interrupted. "So what's the problem?"

"There are photographs, apparently."

My father was shocked. "But nothing happened, you said."

"Still, I compromised myself." Bronstyn looked even more sorrowful.

"Photographs of what exactly? If nothing happened, what's there to photograph?"

"I haven't seen them," Bronstyn said. "Just been told of them. An anonymous note in the mail. But we were together, yes, sometimes…very close. And…she took me on a tour of some of the dance halls where she'd worked. This was strictly business, Harry, believe me, but I was stupid not to have brought a colleague with us. When we got to one of those places, she became frightened, she clung to my arm...

"I told you, Harry, I was careless. These photographs, they'd devastate my wife. They'd do damage to the agency. It's bad, Harry. Very bad."

It was through his eldest brother, my uncle Sam, that my father met and became friendly with Lev Bronstyn.

Sam and Lev had met at Columbia University, where both were pursuing studies in religion, philosophy, literature and the social sciences that would prepare them for the associated rabbinical college, which would follow. They'd become friends perhaps because neither was particularly religious nor had any real interest in the rabbinate. My uncle, who had been given financial support by a friend of the family, saw it as a ticket to education – he graduated but became a journalist, not a rabbi; Lev was dutifully honouring the wishes of his own father, who thirty years earlier had sacrificed his own desire to become a rabbi in order to help support his family. As the two became fast friends, Bronstyn was a frequent visitor at my father's family's apartment on Mott Street.

My father was only eleven or twelve when he met Lev Bronstyn, who was, like Sam, then in his early twenties. There was absolutely no reason for Bronstyn to take a liking to this boy, but he did, and as my father grew into a youth and a young man himself, Bronstyn remained friendly, interested in what my father was doing, willing to lend an ear to his problems, offering advice and support. It was Bronstyn, in fact, who advised my father to leave the city, to go west to try his hand at

Dave Margoshes

the family trade, journalism, far from the shadow of his father and older brother, both of whom were prominent on the Lower East Side – a decision that led to my father spending several years in Cleveland, where he launched his newspaper career. By that time Bronstyn who, ironically, had had a falling out with Sam, had grown from friendly mentor to my father into an actual friend. While my father was away from the city, he and his friend exchanged many letters, and when my father came back to New York, he and Bronstyn began seeing a lot of each other. My father was soon closer to Bronstyn than he ever had been – or would be – with his own brother.

Bronstyn was a tall, somewhat ascetic-looking man with a perpetual hangdog expression broken occasionally by a dolorous smile. My father, describing him to me years later, likened him to "a Jewish Gary Cooper, with a long nose, bright blue eyes – not a handsome man, really, but with a heroic profile." The Cooperesque nose, my father added, had a tendency to drip and was often being wiped, either with a handkerchief or by the back of Bronstyn's wrist.

My father's friend had married a young woman from a good conservative German-Jewish family, much like his own, and by this time had two children, a boy and a girl, and lived in a small house in the Bronx, far from where he worked. It took him almost an hour of travelling by bus and subway to get to and from work every day, but, he told my father, he preferred it that way. "I like to be able to escape from this hellhole completely," he said. "And it gives me perspective."

My father disagreed with his friend's characterization of the Lower East Side, where he worked and had grown up, as a hellhole, but he himself lived at some distance from it, in Coney Island, and there was no disputing that this densely populated corner of Manhattan suffered from more than its share of social ills, all seemingly linked to the pervasive poverty that afflicted the area, including the prostitution with which Bronstyn was so familiar, but also gambling, loansharking and other evils controlled by organized crime. Just walking down a street like Orchard, where my father liked to browse the used bookstores and the pushcarts and horse-drawn wagons of peddlers, with their endless supply of tools, housewares, used books, cheap clothing and *tchotchkas* of all types, was an adventure, dodging the dozens of pickpockets and streetwalkers plying their trades.

It was only natural that, as they moved through the area and among its inhabitants, both my father and Bronstyn should come into occasional contact with gangsters of various stripes.

Just how bad a situation Bronstyn had gotten himself into my father didn't realize until he returned to his office that afternoon and found Hermie, *The Day*'s errand boy, arguing with a younger boy. "Morgenstern," Hermie called to him as he came through the door, "this boy has a package for you. He wouldn't leave it. I told him he could but he wouldn't."

"So here I am," my father said. He turned to the boy, who had the rough and dirty look of the street about him, in suspendered trousers, ill-fitting shoes and cloth cap. "What's so special?"

"I dunno. The man said give this just to you, no one else," the boy said.

"What man was that?"

"I dunno. Just some man on the street. He gave me

a nickel, said you'd give me another." The boy gave Hermie a justified glance.

My father took the package from the boy and gave him the promised nickel. The package, which bore his name in block letters, was no more than a flat manila envelope, the size of a sheet of paper and taped shut. He had a pretty good idea what it would contain but he waited until he got to his desk and sat down before opening it.

There were half a dozen photos, all pretty much the same shot, a man and a woman, glossy, a bit underexposed and out of focus, like the sort of sneak photos some of the English-language tabloids ran on their gossip pages. Photographers often lurked around outside nightclubs in wait for chances at such shots, my father knew. The man in the photo was clearly Lev Bronstyn, the woman an attractive blonde with large white teeth and a bruised air about her. They were standing outside a particularly notorious dance hall on Second Avenue, the *Palais de Danse*, its sign clearly visible. There was nothing inappropriate happening between them but the woman's small hand was placed lightly on Bronstyn's sleeve and her smile suggested she might like there to be.

There was an accompanying note, written in the same crude hand: "Here's your friend, some so-called friend of the 'working girl'." The challenge to run the photos in the paper wasn't stated but didn't need to be.

My father had another friend to whom he often turned when he needed advice. This was Fushgo, a bookseller whose crowded, musty shop was only two blocks further south on East Broadway. My father had only met him recently, since his return to New York, but they had become fast if not close friends.

"It's unthinkable that we should run these photos," my father said.

"Of course, but what are the consequences?" Fushgo asked. He was an older fellow, permanently shaded grey from the settled dust in his shop. Tufts of bristly hair protruded from his ears, causing a persistent itch. "Let's say, just for the sake of argument, you did use them."

"I wouldn't," my father protested.

"But let's say you did."

"It would be a betrayal."

"Exactly," Fushgo said. He twisted a finger in his right ear. "And if you don't?"

My father thought for a moment, his mouth pursed. "After a day or two, I imagine whoever's behind this will give them to the other papers."

"So you can't win," Fushgo observed gloomily.

"No, but the first choice is not really a choice, so the second choice is the only choice. At least it won't be me involved with ruining a friend. Some consolation."

"Also it buys you time," Fushgo said.

"Yes."

"To do what with?"

"That's the question," my father said.

Fushgo gave his ear another twist and glanced at his finger.

"Time is always good," he said.

The next day, which happened to be a Wednesday, my father had lunch at the Garden Cafeteria at the corner of East Broadway and Rutgers Street, as he usually did, then strolled down Canal Street to Allen. It was a warm

Dave Margoshes

day in May, so my father wore his customary suit jacket and tie, but no coat, and his jacket was open. A copy of that afternoon's paper, fresh from the presses, was under his arm.

He paused at the corner and, making an exaggerated show of looking both ways before crossing the street, managed to sneak a quick glance behind him and catch sight of a recognizable face. Since the day before, he'd become familiar with the appearance of two men he didn't know – my father was no detective, but he had a good eye for faces. These two fellows were notable by their very ordinariness, he thought – one was skinny as a minute, with a chisel face and an elongated nose – ironically, somewhat like Bronstyn's; the other hefty, with a face like a chicken dumpling. Both wore workingmen's clothes that made them seem the antithesis of what my father thought of as gangsters, with flashy suits and slicked-back hair. He hadn't seen the two men together but, whenever he was on the street, one or the other seemed to be nearby. It hadn't taken him very long to jump to the conclusion that he was being followed.

The area near *The Day* was, as always, crowded with passersby, so he had no concern for his safety; rather, he was amused and curious. The streets were peopled mostly by men, some in rough working clothes, others in the shiny black suits of the Orthodox, with black felt hats, beards and *payes*, feathery ritual sidelocks. But there were also, my father observed, quite a few women, whose dress advertised them as streetwalkers. Allen Street, which was notorious, was especially infested with these women – there were clots of them at each corner, and individuals leaning at literally every street lamp within sight. On Allen Street and the streets around it, it was said, there were as many brothels as synagogues, if not more; as many women of loose morals as there were pious but weak-willed men.

My father already had some familiarity with gangsters – Arnold Rothstein, reputed to be the head of the city's underworld, and Louis Buchalter, known as Lepke, were both active in the garment trade, on both the bosses' and the unions' sides, as the wind blew, along with a ragtag string of underlings.

He was acquainted with a fellow, a jovial Italian who provided muscle for either side of an argument, depending on who paid the most, whom he considered to be both well connected and discreet. My father had run into him a number of times, had even shared a drink with him once or twice, and knew him to be dangerous but amiable. The evening before, after his conversation with Fushgo, my father had stopped by a certain saloon where he knew this fellow, who was called Two-Fingers Giovanni, liked to spend time – the nickname arose from the unpleasant state of his left hand, rumoured to have come about at the business end of a butcher's cleaver during a youthful fight with a rival gang. Sure enough, he was there, and for the price of a whisky, my father was able to extract the name of the gangster likely behind the photos: Monk Eastman.

"If not Monk himself, then someone who works for him, most likely," Two-Fingers said. "He's got his fingers in every whore this side of the East Side." He grinned. "Well, you know what I mean."

Afterwards, my father had gone back to *The Day*, where he spent some time in the newspaper's dusty morgue, combing through old clippings. As he expected, he was far from the first reporter to have written about prostitution and white slavery. In the years right before the war, there'd been many such exposés, not much different from the ones he'd written. With the war's arrival in 1914, the public's interest had shifted, and there were few stories on the subject until my father had again aroused attention with his tales of Bronstyn's exploits.

My father strolled leisurely along Allen Street, which lay under the heavy shadow of the elevated train tracks, to the corner of Grand, took a right, then another right at Orchard, crowded with pushcarts and hawkers, then another on Hester back to Allen Street. In the course of a walk around the block that should have taken five minutes but instead took twenty, he was propositioned, by his count, thirty-seven times. Their conversations were almost always short – "Hello good-looking," or "Say, there, handsome," in Yiddish inflected with a range of Eastern European accents, Galician, Polish, Hungarian, countered by my father's good-natured reply, "Good afternoon, young lady, no thank you." On Allen Street itself, these conversations were often all but drowned out by the rattle of the elevated train rushing by above them.

One of his two shadows, Chisel Face, was loitering across the street, making a show of studying the contents of a shop window. My father walked quickly across the street and, before he could bolt, had the man by the arm.

"What the hell…" he shouted, wheeling away.

"Take it easy," my father said. "I'm not looking for a fight. I want to talk to Monk Eastman."

"You crazy?" the skinny fellow asked.

"Not at all. Get your friend to go to Eastman, or you do it and your friend can watch me, the heavy-set fellow. I'll stay right here till you return. Don't worry. I don't mean him any harm, or you either. I just want to talk."

"You are crazy," the man said, but a sly grin was spreading across his narrow face. He gestured, and in a few seconds the other fellow came up beside them. The two stepped aside and conferred. After a minute, Chisel Face took off on a trot and Dumpling Face took up a position on the corner, brushing aside a young woman who'd been stationed by the street light. My father, for his part, sat down on the stoop closest to the corner, unfolded his newspaper and began to read.

Half an hour later, my father was ushered by both of his companions through the door of a saloon on Rivington Street, through the crowded saloon itself and into a back room, all but deserted. There, at a large table sat a well-built, dapper man in an expensive silk suit and a meticulous haircut. The man's pleasant face was vaguely familiar.

"Good afternoon, Morgenstern," he said.

"I know you, I think."

"We've met, once or twice, here and there," the other man said. "We have mutual acquaintances." He stood up and extended his hand. "Monk Eastman. I don't know who or what you expected."

My father wasn't altogether surprised that he'd recognized Eastman, or by his manner. As a reporter, he met all sorts of people, didn't always remember them and was no longer surprised by anything he heard or saw. The two men shook hands, and my father took a chair across from Eastman. A bottle was produced, good Scotch, and drinks were poured.

Eastman drank and placed his shot glass down gently. "You wanted to see me?"

"I have a proposition," my father said.

"Go ahead."

"I'm concerned about a friend. He's been a nuisance to you, I gather. But my guess is, not much more than a nuisance, no real harm."

Eastman's expression was politely curious but non-committal.

"Perhaps I've been a nuisance too. I apologize if so. But, you know, if not me, someone else." My father made a hand gesture indicating the power of fate.

"I appreciate that," Eastman said.

My father took a deep breath and drank off his shot of whisky. He preferred rye, but the Scotch was good.

"I don't want to get hurt, but I could be more of a nuisance."

"I imagine."

"So could my friend."

Eastman poured two more drinks. "And your proposition?"

"I think my friend could be persuaded he'd done enough."

The two men observed each other in tense silence. After a minute or two, Eastman drank down his whisky. "No more nuisance, then?"

"And no one gets hurt," my father said. He drank his.

"One more to cement the bargain, Morgenstern?" Eastman asked.

That evening, my father left the *Day* office and headed towards the subway and the train north. He still felt a little light-headed, and elated. He'd called Bronstyn, met him for a coffee at the Café Royale and was satisfied the danger was over. It hadn't been hard to convince his friend that he'd had an effect on the white-slavery problem and to turn his attention to other issues. The problems of unwed mothers and abused women were especially pressing, my father argued. Bronstyn agreed.

"And the photos, they just disappear?" he asked.

"As if they never happened," my father said. He didn't think the photos would actually disappear – Eastman, he thought, was a bit of a gentleman, but certainly no fool – but the threat of their being sent to other newspapers had pretty much evaporated.

At the entrance to the subway, he hesitated, then, changing his direction, headed towards Allen Street. The two men who had been his shadows the past couple of days were no longer to be seen, and he walked slowly, breathing in the bittersweet aroma of what he thought of as the perfume of the Lower East Side, a heady mixture of cooked cabbage, baking bread, sweat, sour meat and horse manure, spiced by the sharp salt aroma of the bay wafting inland on a cool breeze, and enjoying the pastel light of the setting sun that softened the hard edges of the tenement-lined streetscape, imbuing it with a dignity it lacked during the bright glare of day. At Allen, he stopped to admire a trio of young women in bright clothing, engaged in conversation, across the street. He could hear laughter drifting in the light breeze. It was a pleasure, after the long winter, to see women without their coats and boots, mufflers and hats. These three were even showing off a bit of leg. They glanced at him, but didn't stop their conversation.

My father was not intending to purchase their wares – when he was a younger man, in Cleveland, he had indulged once or twice, but now he was content, on a fine evening like this, merely to do a bit of window-shopping.

Dave Margoshes

The Farmhand

When my father was a very young man, not quite twenty-one, he spent one summer in the Catskill Mountains working for a rich family. He liked to say he was a farmhand, and there are a few grainy old photos of him, skinny and shirtless in baggy overalls, pitching a bale of hay, bareback on a horse, and milking a cow – this latter the only photo I've ever seen of my usually reserved father grinning. But the truth is that, while he did do some farm work, his primary responsibility that summer was to tutor the children of the family. This was a delicious irony, as my father had dropped out of school himself in the fifth grade, when he was thirteen. Any knowledge and skills he may have possessed that would make him qualified to be a tutor he had acquired on his own and were hard-earned.

He didn't know, when he accepted the job, that he would be drawn into an early skirmish of the Great War; would come close to becoming one of its first casualties.

My father's father was an eminent journalist on the Lower East Side, editor of the conservative daily *The Morning Journal*, and my uncle Sam, my father's eldest brother, was also working on a newspaper, *The Day*, and beginning to establish a reputation as a columnist. My father too had dreams of being a writer, though he thought he'd rather write novels and poems than fodder for newspapers. "What would you write *about?*" my grandfather asked him when my father told him of his ambitions, and this was very much on his mind for many years afterwards. Certainly it was on this day, as he contemplated the possibility of an adventure outside the city.

It was through Sam that my father made the acquaintance of the Pearlman family. They were German Jews who had already been in New York for three generations, having arrived before the Civil War, and were well established in social as well as business circles, completely Americanized. Hershell Pearlman, one of three brothers with diverse interests, was a lawyer; it was he whom my uncle was friendly with. A younger brother, Robert, had taken over his grandfather's jewelry shop on Park Avenue, and it was he who was seeking a tutor.

The only real requirements for the job were fluencies in both English and Yiddish and a willingness to spend time with children, my father was told. These were qualifications he had. Familiarity with farm chores would be a plus, and he had some of that as well. For my father, the thought of spending the summer in the country, far from the stink and steamy heat of the city, was a delight. He had spent his early childhood on a farm, and, though it had been a mean life, one his family was anxious to escape, he harboured some nostalgic memories that made the prospects of spending the summer of his twenty-first year on a farm especially appealing.

It was the last week in June of 1914 and the sun was shining brightly, the air fragrant with the scents of early summer mixed with exhaust fumes from the endless procession of taxicabs and streetcars on Park Avenue and manure announcing the presence of horse-drawn wagons on the side streets. My father, who had walked north from Mott Street, where he was still living with his parents, younger brothers and unmarried sister, arrived at the jewelry shop at the appointed time, wearing an ill-fitting woolen suit he'd borrowed from his father. My father was two inches taller than my grandfather and his ankles and wrists protruded from the sleeves and cuffs, making him look somewhat like a stick figure drawn by a child. His curly black hair crackled with electricity from the unused-to brushing it had just received at the hands of his sister Ida.

He stopped on the corner of Forty-seventh Street, a half block south of the shop, where a noisy crowd was milling around a newsboy. The banner headline on the *New York Herald* proclaimed the assassination of Archduke Ferdinand of Austria. My father gave the boy a penny and put the folded paper under his arm, thinking it would add to the overall impression he hoped to make. Beyond that, though, he gave little thought to the day's news.

A clerk ushered my father to the rear of the shop, where he found Pearlman, a tidy man in his late thirties with a well-trimmed moustache, impeccably dressed in a fawn-coloured suit, examining a glittering stone of some sort through a jeweller's monocle. "Ah, young Harry," he said, removing the monocle from his eye and rising to shake hands, but through the interview that followed my father persisted in the feeling that he was being examined in just such a thorough, microscopic manner as the stone had been.

The interview was short and seemingly undemanding. "Tell me something about yourself," Pearlman asked after they'd been seated on either side of an impressive oak desk.

There was little to tell but my father tried. He'd come to America with his family when he was ten, from Galicia, a troubled corner of what was then the Austro-Hungarian Empire, over which the Archduke

Ferdinand – just murdered – had ruled. As a boy on the farm his family rented, he had often helped the hired workmen with milking cows, collecting eggs and shooing the geese, and at this news Pearlman smiled approvingly. He had learned reading and writing and other subjects from a succession of young rabbinical students who came to the farm three afternoons a week – it pleased him no end that, should he win this position, he'd be doing much the same as his own tutors. In New York, he'd attended three grades at the public school on Henry Street, just a few blocks from where his family lived, leaving at thirteen, when his English was good enough, to work. Since then, he'd had a succession of minor jobs, delivering newspapers, selling papers on street corners, running errands at his father's office, helping a milkman on his early morning delivery rounds, wielding a shovel on a crew repairing city streets, planting and tending trees in Central Park as part of another city crew. For the last year or more he'd been employed as an apprentice silversmith for the famous Tiffany company but was feeling restless, wanting to better himself. As he told this, his cheeks suddenly reddened, for it occurred to him that Pearlman, a jeweller, might take offence, but if he had he didn't betray it.

My father didn't say why he worked: so that Sam and his brother Henry, one year younger than him, could attend university, so that Ida could study to be a midwife, so that his brother Izzy, who was still in high school, could also go to college when his time came. Somehow, it had fallen to my father and his brother Nathan, one year older, to help provide for their siblings. Over this apparent injustice, he felt no bitterness. His own time, he was certain, would come.

"And when you are not working?" Pearlman inquired. "In the evenings? You have friends, I suppose?"

Friends, yes, my father said, and he also took night classes at the *Arbiter Ring* – the Workman's Circle – and read everything he could get his hands on. And, he admitted, his cheeks suddenly reddening again, he often, on his own time, wrote stories and poems.

Pearlman listened intently, and when my father came to an embarrassed halt, the jeweller made only this comment: "Your English is excellent." Then he asked him to repeat what he'd said, as best he could, in Yiddish.

This my father did, with no difficulty, since he was equally fluent in both languages. He also mentioned, though he wasn't asked this, that he could speak Polish passably and had a smattering of German.

"Ah," Pearlman said with satisfaction. "And Hebrew?"

Here my father had to admit he had knowledge of only a few words.

"You were not *bar mitzvah?*" Pearlman asked with some surprise, perhaps because he knew my father had a brother who was a rabbi.

"No," my father said, with a mixture of self-consciousness and defiance.

"So you won't object to working on the Sabbath?"

"Certainly not."

"This is very satisfactory," Pearlman said.

As my father was rising to go, Pearlman noticed the headline on the folded paper my father had placed on the chair beside him. He picked up the paper and quickly read the first few paragraphs.

"This is terrible news," he said gravely, "terrible. I've been afraid something like this might happen." He looked at my father knowingly, but my father had only the vaguest understanding of the implications of the news.

"Thank God, this will all seem very far away from

Mohegan Lake," Pearlman concluded, shaking my father's hand.

Within a few days, my father was on a train upstate to Peekskill, where he was met at the station by Mrs. Pearlman, a tall, graceful woman in a brocaded dress, with the scent of lilacs clinging to her, and was driven in a magnificent four-door Dodge touring sedan to the Pearlman country home, at Mohegan Lake, a further distance of some fifteen miles. My father had ridden in streetcars, of course, but he'd never been in either a train or an automobile, let alone one driven by a woman, let alone a woman as enthralling as Mrs. Pearlman, and his head was spinning by the time they arrived at the estate, where a barking black and white sheepdog raced out to greet them. He was ushered through the front door of a large house sheltered by a ring of imposing oak trees.

There he was introduced to Betty, a local woman who cooked and cleaned at the house, and the two children, Benjamin, who was seven, and Esther, who was five. They eagerly clambered around him, the boy peppering him with questions, the girl offering for his inspection a red-headed doll.

"We'll have lots of fun," my father assured the children.

He had noticed a stream flowing beneath a bridge they had crossed just before arriving at the house, and he asked Benjy if he had a fishing pole. "When I was your age I loved to fish in the pond on our farm," my father told the boy. "It's been a while, but you don't forget how."

Then he asked the children which was their favourite subject: reading, writing or arithmetic. They looked at him blankly.

"Oh, the children are on vacation for the summer," Mrs. Pearlman said lightly, and she sang, slightly off-key:

"No more pencils, no more books, no more teacher's dirty looks." Like her husband, she was in her thirties, but looked younger, with long honey-brown hair that she wore loose around her shoulders like a schoolgirl, and startling green eyes set off by a complexion that was pale and flawless. By this time, my father, who had not yet been with a woman, had fallen deliriously in love with her. The dizziness this caused added to his confusion.

"Then what...?" he began.

"Didn't my husband explain?" Mrs. Pearlman asked, exasperated. "Your job is merely to talk to the children. In Yiddish."

The children were sent outside to play and she explained the situation. Her husband's family had originally been German speakers, but over the years in New York had lost most of their knowledge of that language. English was what they spoke at business, at home, with their friends. Her husband knew no Yiddish beyond a few words, and, my father realized, had listened to his discourse without any real comprehension. But Mrs. Pearlman was a Litvak. She had come to America, to Chicago, as an infant with her parents, who were Yiddish speakers and never mastered the language of their new county, but she herself had grown up speaking English in school and, having left home early for college, a brief career as a designer, then marriage, her Yiddish was very rusty. The children, therefore, had none at all. Even the nanny-cum-housekeeper the family employed in New York was no help – she was a Negro woman from the South.

Now here, she explained to my father, was where things became complicated. She and her parents had been estranged for many years. "I won't go into it," she said, giving my father a frank look. "You seem to be an intelligent man. I'm sure you can imagine."

Actually, my father had no idea what she was talking about, but he gave her his complete, rapt attention.

"Now, through a most fortuitous circumstance, I've become reconciled with my parents. I've been to see them. They're invited here and will be visiting in August. They're old now. My father..." She hesitated. "Things are different. Middle of August. That's when they're to arrive. That gives you more than six weeks."

My father's job, he realized, was to familiarize the children with Yiddish so that they could speak to their grandparents, whom they were about to meet for the first time. "I could do it myself," Mrs. Pearlman said, "but my Yiddish is so poor I'd just be giving them bad habits, I'm sure. And children don't listen to their mother anyway." She laughed gaily. "I just want you to spend time with them, as a big brother would. The Yiddish aside, we'd been thinking of hiring someone as a companion to them. There are no other children in the vicinity, and Benjy and Esther were so restless and lonely last summer. So talk to them, play with them, take them places, go fishing with them, as you suggested, but speak to them in Yiddish. And make sure they learn to speak to you."

"Watch that Holstein, Harry!" Schmidt snapped impatiently.

It didn't take much to set the farm manager off. When this happened, due to my father's slowness or clumsiness or failure to understand and execute a command immediately, his already ruddy cheeks grew even redder and a vein in his thick neck jumped.

My father frowned but said nothing. Dealing with

Dave Margoshes

found himself most looking forward to in the day, most cherishing afterwards. Unless it was cool and rainy, in which case cocktails were served in the living room, in front of a fire, the adults would meet on the screened-in porch, which faced west to the meadow and pond, and from which splendid sunsets could be observed safe from mosquitoes. Hillary mixed martinis and, pouring a glass for my father, her hands always brushed against his, deliberately, he was sure. When Robert Pearlman was at home, of course, his position as head of the household was clear, and he set the tone and dominated the conversation. But in his absence, anarchy reigned on the Pearlman porch during cocktail hour, or so it seemed to my father. Hillary and Betty often sat together on a wicker sofa, their knees pressed together like school-girls, and chattered about what my father thought of as womanly matters: cooking, clothes, the children. My father, who invariably sat in a green Adirondack chair across from them, would sometimes be drawn into these light conversations, though he had little to say. Schmidt preferred to stand, pacing restlessly around the room and offering brief occasional pronouncements on the weather, the state of the crops, politics or, invariably, the growing threat of war in Europe.

"When it comes," he liked to predict, "there will be no standing on the sidelines. Will we be with Germany? Or against her? Harry, where will you stand?"

If Robert Pearlman was present, this was sure to provoke a spirited argument. He was opposed to war, and if there was one, he believed, England and the Americas should stay well clear of it.

Of more interest to my father than the conversation was the exchange of glances that ricocheted around the cozy room, especially in Robert's absence. He, of course, could not help but cast fleeting looks of adoration at

Hillary, try though he did to keep them furtive. For her part, Mrs. Pearlman usually ignored these looks, but occasionally she would raise her head and meet his gaze, returning his timid glance with what he was sure was a meaningful one of her own. But meaning what?

My father also became aware that Betty, cheerful, innocent Betty, was similarly casting glances in his direction, and her manner with him was frequently nothing short of flirtatious. And it was patently obvious that Schmidt was gazing, as often as he decently could, at the wife of his employer, all the while attempting to divert attention by running his hand across his smoothly shaven chin. It also gradually became obvious to my father that Schmidt, when not gazing at Hillary, was scowling at him, and that his rancour seemed to grow in direct proportion to the amount of attention that Mrs. Pearlman gave him.

Years later, when my father would tell this story, he would remark at this point that it was only his youth and inexperience that prevented him from being overwhelmed by the sexual *frisson* and intrigue darting like dragonflies after mosquitoes beneath the slowly turning fan in the Pearlman porch as, outside, darkness gently fell over the countryside.

The stream my father had noticed the first day had been dammed at the end of the meadow, creating a pond where the cows drank, pausing in their endless chewing to dip their dark muzzles deep into the water. The pond was remarkably like the one my father remembered from the family farm in Galicia. There were small fish and eels in the pond, and my father and Benjy became expert at luring them with worms and minnows. As a boy, half a world away, he'd fished with a stick cut from a branch and a string. Now, just a decade later, he and Benjy made use of new rods and tackle that Pearlman had purchased in the city for them. Even Esther enjoyed the fishing, though she couldn't bear to touch either bait or fish. As the summer progressed, Betty became equally expert at turning the fish into a succession of memorable meals. Even the unpleasant-looking eels, when cooked in a soup with lots of salt and pepper, were made pleasing by her clever hands.

"What, are we becoming Catholics, fish on Friday?" Robert Pearlman jokingly complained the first time he enjoyed the fruits of these fishing expeditions, and he tousled his son's hair, causing Benjy to squirm with pleasure. "Harry, you're supposed to be teaching them Yiddish, not Latin."

Later, this joking complaint was picked up by Schmidt, who darkened it into "What, fish again?" and then, "Not fish *again!*" But, my father noticed, Schmidt always ate every bite.

As they lounged by the pond in the July heat, their poles by their sides, my father and the children chattered as if he were indeed their big brother, talking about fish, baseball (Benjy was mad for the Yankees, then suffering a string of losses) and anything else that came into their heads. They went for walks about the farm, played catch, threw sticks for the tireless sheepdog, *Kalev*, which was Hebrew for "dog," and took rides on the broad back of the gentle *Yarmulke*. And my father told story after story, of life on the farm in Galicia, of the trip across the Atlantic, of life on the Lower East Side, which, to the children, was as foreign as what he referred to as "the old country."

From the beginning, my father would speak to the children in Yiddish, first putting names to simple things – rock, pants, sky, dog – then incorporating them into simple sentences. As Hillary had specified, he didn't bother with the niceties of grammar, spelling or anything to do with the reading or writing of the language. This was strictly conversational Yiddish, and the children were quick learners. By the end of July, he had them chattering away as if Yiddish were their mother tongue – at least, that's what Hillary remarked. She was very pleased, and she put her hand on my father's and squeezed it warmly as she said so.

"You've done wonders with them, Harry. You should consider a career in languages. Perhaps you should start thinking about college."

My father blushed with pleasure. "All I do is talk to them," he said truthfully. There was neither skill nor guile involved.

The date for the arrival of the grandparents drew closer and the children's excitement grew.

"What will they be like?" Benjy wanted to know.

"Will they love me?" Esther asked.

My father told the children about his own grandparents, his mother's parents, whom he had last seen on the day he, his mother and his brothers Izzy, Nathan and Henry set out by ox cart from their village for Amsterdam – a long, ardous trip of several weeks – to take ship to America to join his father, Sam and Ida, who had gone a year earlier. He had kissed them goodbye, first his *bubba*, on her cheek, then his *zaida*, on his forehead because his beard tickled, knowing that he would probably never see them again. My father had cried that day, though he didn't tell the children that. Instead, he said, "There were no tears, because they were so happy for us."

"But weren't you sad?" Esther asked.

"Yes, of course, I was very sad," my father said.

"And is it true, you never saw them again?" Benjy asked. He was speaking Yiddish and he chose his words carefully.

"Yes," my father said.

"And they're dead now?" Esther asked. The children already had some knowledge of this concept, having helped my father bury several dead birds they'd found.

"Yes," said my father, "and that's why it's so important that you should meet your grandparents now, while you have the chance. They're old."

"And is it true that Mommy hasn't seen her Mommy and Daddy for years and years?"

"That's right, Esthela." My father took the little girl in his arms. "Do you ever get mad at Mommy? Or at Daddy?"

"Sometimes."

My father smiled. "And you, Benjy?"

"Sometimes."

"And do you sometimes get so mad you think, 'I wish they were dead,' or think about running away and never coming home, just to show them, to make them feel bad?"

The children pouted. Esther sucked her thumb. My father gently tugged at her hand until it came away. "Tell the truth now."

"Sometimes," Benjy said.

"...times," Esther echoed.

"You have to be careful what you wish for," my father said. "Sometimes wishes come true and you don't like it so much and you can't take them back."

"Is that what Mommy did?" Esther asked.

"What do you think?" my father asked.

My father was milking. He sat on the stool, his head pressed against the warm side of the cow, his fingers wrapped around the teats, squeezing, that peculiar rhythm as if they were an instrument and he was making music.

Over the last week, the festering situation in Europe had erupted into full-fledged hostilities, with war being declared between Germany and Russia on the first day of August, followed, in rapid succession, by German invasions of France and Poland, and Britain joining the fray a day later. At breakfast just that morning, they had heard on the radio that Russian troops had crossed the border into Prussia and an Eastern Front was fully inflamed, including Austria-Hungary and Serbia. Although the fighting was far away from Peekskill, it was possible for my father to imagine troops marching through the village where, just ten years ago, he had lived as a boy.

Naturally, he was upset, and confused. News reports from Washington suggested that the United States was unlikely to become involved, at least not for a while, and it was unclear whether someone like my father, a native of an area under arms, or soon to be, would be expected to fight in any event. He was anxious to return to New York and be with his family, but had promised the Pearlmans he would stay until Hillary's parents' arrival, scheduled in just a week's time.

Already the situation at the Pearlmans' estate was becoming ugly.

The previous evening, at dinner, Robert Pearlman, home for the weekend, and Ernst Schmidt had engaged in a bitter argument, Schmidt, predictably, on the side of Germany, Pearlman favouring the Allies. The fact that the Pearlman family had lived for generations in Germany before immigrating to the United States did not mitigate his views one bit. The argument had ended with Schmidt calling his employer "a colonial apologist," the women and children in tears and Pearlman ordering the farm manager out of his house, Betty rushing after him. There were no nightcaps that night, nor did either of the Schmidts come to the house for breakfast. Earlier, Schmidt had been in the barn as usual when my father arrived for the morning milking, lightning bolts blazing from his reddened eyes, or so it seemed to my father, but the two men had managed to avoid each other. Oscar, the part-time hired man, was there to help out, as was usual on a Saturday.

My father, who had no head for politics, had stayed out of the argument, saying barely a word through dinner, then going directly to his room after helping Hillary put the agitated children to bed. He had wanted to say something comforting to her, perhaps to put his hand gently on her shoulder, but he had resisted, instead willing his attention to be focused on Benjy and Esther. For a moment, as they adjusted the covers on Esther's bed, Hillary on one side, my father on the other, she gave him a look that confused him. He lay awake in bed for hours wondering if it had conveyed desire or simply gratitude.

Breakfast had been quiet, the children still sulky, Betty conspicuously absent from the kitchen. Ordinarily, on a Saturday, Schmidt, who seemed indifferent to religion, would drive the Pearlmans into Peekskill for morning services at the synagogue, but there was no mention of such a trip today.

The day passed uneventfully, my father occupied with the children, who had many questions. They wanted to know why their father and Mr. Schmidt, as they called him, had argued, what war was, where Germany and Russia and France and the other countries they were suddenly hearing about were. My father found an atlas in the library and spent a long time with the children pointing out key locations and, in as simple a way as he could, explaining geopolitics. This actually calmed him, since it helped to clarify his own thinking on the situation in Europe.

On a map of Germany, he showed the children Berlin and Leipzig, where he knew the Pearlmans had originated, and other geographical points. He showed them, on a large map of eastern Europe, Lithuania, from whence their mother's family came, and the area of the Austro-Hungarian Empire straddling parts of Poland and the Ukraine where he and his own family had lived.

"Why do people move around so much?" Benjy wanted to know.

"They want a better life," my father answered. "For themselves, and especially their children."

"Why are bad people so dumb dumb?" Esther asked petulantly, and my father laughed.

"Only God knows that, Esthela."

The Schmidts had remained out of sight most of the day. But as it was Saturday, that wasn't unusual. The Pearlman household wasn't particularly religious, but other than the basic farm chores there was no work done on the place, and meals were simple, and usually cold, sliced meats from a delicatessen in Peekskill or cheese and bread and fruit. That's what the meals had been this Saturday, and there was little talk at the table. Even Robert Pearlman, usually garrulous, was quiet and, save for one moment at dinner when he gave my father a long appraising look, kept his eyes on his plate. My father's own eyes, as furtively as he could manage, strayed often to Hillary's lovely face, but her eyes too were mostly lowered.

When my father came to the barn for the evening milking, there was no sign of Schmidt. Even Oscar was nowhere to be seen.

He brought in the cows, with the help of the yapping dog, and locked them into their stanchions. Milking all of them by himself would take a while, and they would soon be bellowing with impatience, but he knew he could do it. He didn't want to bother Pearlman, and doubted if the jeweller could milk a cow at any rate.

He was on the third cow, one of the Guernseys, and the rich smell of warm milk rising from the pail was beginning to intoxicate him, when he became aware of the presence of someone nearby. He turned his head, raising his eyes, to see Schmidt leaning against the barn wall, watching him with a jaundiced eye.

"So you choose to remain a lackey, Harry," the farm manager said scornfully. The smell of whisky wafted off him like a cloud of flies around a cow's head.

"I choose to do what is expected of me," my father replied simply. He went on with the milking.

Schmidt was wearing his jodhpurs and boots as usual, and, my father noticed with some alarm, held the shotgun loosely against his hip.

"I can't abide this fool Pearlman, this traitor, another minute," he said, ignoring my father's comment. "Betty and I leave for New York in the morning, then on to Germany. You'd be well advised to do the same."

My father was acutely conscious of the shotgun, and of Schmidt's volatility, but he had made up his mind not to be bullied.

"This is our country now," he said, resting his head against the Guernsey's flank. "And it's definitely Betty's country."

"You're a fool," Schmidt replied mildly. He made no move. "And my wife is none of your business."

"*I'm* the fool?"

The two men eyed each other, with suspicion and contempt, until my father finished with the Guernsey, slapping her affectionately on the rump as he rose. He moved the stool and pail down the row to the next cow, a Jersey that rolled her tongue and shook her head with impatience. "Okay, Bossy, good girl," my father murmured soothingly. The tension between the two men was palpable, the silence broken now only by the hissing of milk into the pail.

"Harry..." Schmidt began, his tone menacing, and he took a step forward, the shotgun rising involuntarily with his movement, but before he could say another word or my father could react, there was a rattle from the barn door. Oscar stood there, his usual good-natured but baffled grin on his vacant face. "Late," he said with a shrug of his broad shoulders. "Sleep."

"Grab a pail," my father said. Relief coursed through him, and he buried his face in the cow's warm hide for a moment. When he looked up, Schmidt was gone.

The milking done, my father bade Oscar good night and paused on his way to the house for a moment in the empty barnyard, wiping his hands. Although it was only early evening, the sun was already low and red in the sky to the west – it was August and days were getting noticeably shorter. The days remained hot but evenings were cooler and it was easier to sleep. With Schmidt and Betty gone, he imagined the Pearlmans might want him to stay on longer to help with the chores until something else could be arranged, maybe even through the grandparents' visit. He would do that, he resolved, do whatever was asked of him. But soon his time on the farm would end and he'd be returning to the city and, as was becoming increasingly evident, an uncertain future. He had no way of knowing that his time with the Pearlmans would serve him well and that once again he'd be working on a farm.

He looked over to the silent Pearlman house, where no lights glowed. The Schmidt house was similarly unlit, but he could hear, from within its walls, shouting, a man's gruff bark, followed by a woman's high keen. Then silence. It was hard to believe that Betty would really follow Schmidt to Germany, but the depth of mystery that surrounded women continued to confound and astound him. He shook his head in puzzlement. There was another shout, and a clatter from the Schmidt house, as if dishes or pots had been thrown against a wall.

My father stood motionless in the dusk.

The Wisdom of Solomon

There he was in Cleveland. My father liked to use this expression for his life in those days: "I was still chasing the donkey, trying to pin the tail to it." The donkey had led him away from New York and out west, where his intention was to see some of the world and, hopefully, write about it. But he'd gotten no further than Chicago, where he holed up in a cheap hotel room for several weeks and wrote, in longhand, the bulk of a novel, a fanciful tale of a sensitive boy growing up in the Lower East Side that owed much to Joyce's *Portrait of an Artist as a Young Man*. When his money ran out, he burned the manuscript – a surprisingly satisfying ritual – and he circled back to Cleveland, where he'd heard, from a poet fleeing the place, of a job on a Yiddish newspaper. His father and brother were both well-known journalists, and it had been important for him to make his own name, on his own, and he'd gone so far, once he got to Cleveland, as actually to change his name, to Morgenstern, which means morning star. Now, at last, he had his first real job on a newspaper, though it wasn't quite what he had expected, and was beginning what he hoped would be a glorious career. If not glorious, then at least exciting, interesting. He saw himself as Don Quixote, the hero of the famous novel he had recently read, tilting at windmills – righting wrongs – not with a lance but a pen. First, though, he had to learn to type.

And he held in his hands the hearts of thousands

of readers. That was his chief concern.

"My husband beats me and the children. What should I do?"

A reader had posed this question in a letter and my father considered his answer with gravity. If he advised her to be a dutiful wife and bear what her husband meted out, he might be sentencing her to a life of drudgery, frustration and pain, and possibly even worse for the children. On the other hand, what if he suggested she leave the man – what sort of life would she and her children face, without a roof over their heads and a source of food, clothing and protection? Even the middle ground was fraught with danger, he could see: should he urge her to talk to her husband, to try to mollify him, she might instead provoke him into even more extreme acts of violence. Lives might well hang in the balance.

How to respond?

It was 1920, and my father was twenty-seven; as he liked to say, he was always a few years older than the century.

The Cleveland Jewish World – Der Velt – had a grand title, but the paper itself was somewhat less than grand. Its circulation was barely fifty thousand, just a fraction of that of the big Yiddish dailies of New York City, but it saw itself playing a role just as important in the lives of the Jews of Cleveland and other cities in Ohio, bringing them not just news but education, entertainment and literature. It was that part that most interested my father, who had been writing a novel and poems, but he was assigned more mundane tasks at first, not the least of which were obituaries. He got a crash course in the history of Cleveland as he succinctly documented the lives of its Jewish residents as they

Dave Margoshes

died. "People are dying to get into our pages," my father's boss, Everett Heshberg, told him. "It's the last time most of them ever will. Some of them, the first time too. Treat them with respect."

My father's chief job, though, was as news writer, another grand title that was somewhat less than it sounded. *The World* subscribed to the Associated Press news wire, which, of course, came in English. First thing in the morning, Heshberg, who as managing editor was the heart and soul of the paper, went through the overnight dispatches, selecting stories he thought would be of interest to his readers. This included local items of government, politics, human interest and even crime – the same stories which that day would appear (or already had the previous day) in the front pages of *The Cleveland Plain Dealer*, which had, in fact, originated most of the local and state AP items. He also selected many stories from Europe, which was still recovering and reorganizing from the ravages of the Great War. Cleveland's Jews came from many parts of Europe – Germany, Romania, Russia, Hungary, Latvia, Galicia and elsewhere – and were hungry for news of home, even if they no longer really considered those distant countries their homes.

My father and another young man, who was somewhat senior to him, shared the translation duties, which he enjoyed. The trick was not so much to translate literally as to read the story, absorb it and write it fresh in Yiddish as if the story were his own. My father was ideally suited for such a task, as he was fluent in both English and Yiddish, and could write quickly, though his two-finger attack at the typewriter was the cause of much amusement in *The World* newsroom. When he had time to spare, he practiced ten-finger typing but it seemed hopeless.

There was little spare time, though. *The World* was an afternoon paper, meaning it appeared on the street shortly after noon. My father reported for work at six in the morning and wrote news till the nine-thirty deadline. Then he turned his attention to the death notices sent in by the Jewish funeral homes. As Heshberg had explained it to him, "Each death represents a life, and each life is a story." Again, my father's job was to translate, taking the bare essentials of those lives – the facts provided by the families for the mortuaries – and turn them into interesting stories, occasionally taking liberties.

"Do not fabricate," Heshberg counselled, "but bend."

This suited my father fine, for he was attempting, as he saw it, to tailor the soul of a poet into the mind of a journalist. Each obituary, in his hands, became a poem.

News and obituaries occupied almost all of my father's time – after that day's paper was put to bed, as the expression went, the process would immediately begin again for the next day's edition – but they took up only a small part of the paper, which was mostly filled with articles by real writers on all manner of subjects: essays on philosophical and theological subjects, usually written by learned rabbis; treatises on history, civics and politics; and educational articles that helped the Jewish immigrant community of Ohio in establishing their lives in this new world: how to apply for citizenship, how to get a driver's licence, the rights of a tenant and so on. Then there were poems, short stories, condensed novels, literary criticism. This is what my father aspired to but he knew he had to earn the right to it. So he was both thrilled and chagrined when Heshberg asked him to write the advice column.

The newspapers of New York were filled with such columns, which were wildly popular. Abe Cahan, the great editor at *The Forward*, the Socialist paper, had invented the form, which he called the *Bintel Brief*, Yiddish for a bundle of letters, but all the other Yiddish papers had followed, even the religious papers, which at first considered themselves too serious for such a seemingly trivial feature. But readers demanded it. Regardless of what paper they read, they had questions, often much the same ones. Even the English papers, like the *Sun* and the *Telegram* in New York, seeing all the fuss, were quick to follow.

Native-born readers and well-established immigrants, though, were less likely to pose the utilitarian questions of the recent arrivals, so the columns established by the English papers quickly narrowed their focus to the lovelorn. Heshberg made it clear to my father that his column would involve much more than just letters from unhappy lovers. This was just as well, since my father, who was still a bachelor, was one of the least likely men on earth to give advice on affairs of the heart, as soon would be evident.

"There should be nothing to it for a smart fellow like you, Morgenstern," Heshberg said. My father recognized the flattery as a ploy, but he was flattered just the same. "You have the intelligence and sensitivity for the job," the editor continued. "Just as in the obituaries, every life is a story. Every letter is an opportunity for you to influence those lives. Think of yourself as having a conversation with the readers, a conversation about their deepest concerns, worries, fears. Think of yourself as a rabbi."

That was exactly what was frightening my father. The last thing he wanted to be was a rabbi, a calling that his eldest brother, Sam, had studied but hadn't followed, but the notion of a conversation with the readers was appealing to him.

Heshberg had already determined that my father's own identity, and that of any subsequent writers assigned this task, would be concealed. To this end, he had concocted a fictitious advisor called Yenta Schmegge, a name which, with its play on the hapless sadsack Jewish figure of the *shmegegge,* he hoped would convey a combination of humour and seriousness readers would find appealing. My father would assume the persona of Yenta as he composed replies to the letter-writers. When he tired of the assignment, "after six months or a year," Heshberg said, another writer would take his place and consistency would be maintained.

My father agreed to all this – he was relieved that he would not have to put his own name on his replies – and even agreed to Heshberg's plan to prime the pump during the first days that the column would run, although he objected at first.

"Make up letters?" He realized immediately that his aghast tone might be offensive to the editor. "What I mean is..."

"You're concerned about the ethics of the situation, Morgenstern?" Heshberg looked at him with a frank expression, but he didn't appear hostile.

"Well, yes."

"Ethics don't really enter into it, don't you see? This isn't news. It's what in the English papers they call features. What if it were a short story or a novel you were writing?"

"That would be fiction," my father said.

"Lies, you mean?"

"No." My father hesitated. He recalled a definition of fiction he had heard from a well-known novelist during a heated discussion over coffee at a crowded table

Dave Margoshes

at the Café Royale in New York. "Made up, yes, but in the service of truth."

"Exactly," Heshberg said. "You see my point exactly."

"I see."

"Just make them believable," Heshberg said. "Don't worry. In a week's time your desk will be covered with letters. Real ones."

My father thought long and hard, taking long late-night walks on deserted streets near his rooming house, staring thoughtfully into his glass of beer at the nearby tavern. As it turned out, the first few questions and answers he wrote proved to be so sensational they immediately helped make the column a success, but one of them – the very first – also returned to cause my father some discomfort later on.

For his first column, he wrote this letter:

> *Esteemed editor,*
> *Please help me!*
> *I am a nineteen-year-old woman, in good health, well-proportioned, attractive, or so men have told me. I come from a good, religious family. My blessed parents and my precious brothers and sisters love me. But now they have threatened to disown me!*
> *I am in love with a Red Indian man, a member of one of the Ohio tribes. He is a good man, educated in a government school, and refined, not a wild savage. He claims that his people are one of the Lost Tribes of Israel, that he is a Jew! I have no reason to disbelieve him.*
> *He knows little of Judaism but he seeks to learn. I love this man and want to marry him and together make a good, devout Jewish family. But my family say he is a charlatan and that I will be dead to them should I follow my heart.*

> *I cannot give up this man, but I cannot bear the thought of losing my family. What should I do?*
> *A distraught reader.*

This was followed by a painstakingly careful reply, written with Heshberg's admonition in mind: "Avoid extremes. Take the middle ground whenever possible. Provoke but do not enrage":

> *Dear distraught reader,*
> *Your dilemma is certainly a profound and unique one, though it points to a more universal problem, namely: how shall Jewry interact with the world? Shall we seek to preserve our unique identity, as the Chosen People of God? Or should we attempt to take our part within the larger Brotherhood of Man, in which all are equal?*
> *This is a question for the rebbinim to ponder and debate, for philosophers, not politicians, and certainly not journalists. It is an old debate, and shows no sign of abating. As to your specific problem, we can only advise you to follow your heart, and wish you well.*

As he'd been instructed, he finished the letter with the words "With love, Yenta Schmegge."

My father stood nervously beside Heshberg's desk as the editor read his typewritten copy, filled with the inevitable XXXd-over typing mistakes. He raised his head, a broad smile on his usually placid face. He had a thin moustache that was several shades darker than his unruly salt and pepper hair, as if he had run the tip of a pencil back and forth against it a number of times.

"Brilliant, Morgenstern. Or should I call you Solomon? This is the stuff."

On the spot, Heshberg decided to change the title

of the advice column from "With Love from Yenta" to "The Wisdom of Solomon," though the former would remain as the signature. My father went back to his typewriter with his heart soaring.

"The Wisdom of Solomon" was indeed what the column was titled when it appeared the following Monday and in days to come, always prominently displayed on the second page, above the obituaries, although within the offices of *The World* it continued to be referred to as "the Schmegge."

The letter from the woman in love with the Indian ran that Monday and others that my father had concocted in the days that followed, but the week was not even out before the first real letters began to arrive, by hand and then through the post, and, as Heshberg had predicted, by the following week a steady stream of letters was arriving and my father no longer had to concoct lives wracked with heartbreaking dilemmas. Instead, the time allotted to this task was more than taken up by reading through the letters, selecting a couple of good ones for each day and writing the replies.

The replies, he found, were considerably easier to write than the concocted letters, but, though he had felt ambivalent about writing those letters, when they were no longer necessary, he missed them.

Many of the real letters were considerably more mundane, dealing with disputes with landlords, employers and bureaucrats, like the man who wrote to complain about the barking of a dog in the night. My father's replies were instructive ("What is more important, the good will of a neighbour or a few extra minutes of sleep?" he inquired rhetorically), and thus played an important role, as Heshberg frequently reminded him, but they took no imagination or creative powers. To the question from a woman about the proper handling of garbage being put out for collection, for example, he merely telephoned the appropriate clerk at City Hall and quickly had the answer, just as the letter writer herself could have done, except that, perhaps, her command of English was not up to it.

"You are the reader's agent," Heshberg had instructed.

There were also questions relating to child rearing, education, career choices, immigration, housing and a variety of other issues as well as, always, those of a romantic nature. There was never any telling what the day's mail would bring, and my father was often hard pressed in producing answers that were both informative and entertaining, which was what his editor expected of him.

Despite the ordinariness of the majority of the letters the column received, there were always some letters, "gems," my father called them, that echoed those of his own creation during the first week.

"Most worthy editor," one man, who signed himself "Tormented and Torn," wrote, "I have been unfaithful to my beloved wife. Should I kill myself? Confess all and suffer the consequences? Or keep my own counsel and let God deal with me as He will?"

My father was delighted. "My dear Tormented, By all means, put thoughts of suicide far from your mind. But at the same time, mend your ways. Being unfaithful once does not give you licence to be unfaithful again," he replied in a column that quickly became known and was often quoted. "Bad enough the unfaithfulness to your wife. Do not compound the sin by being unfaithful to God."

He wrote more, jabbing furiously at the typewriter keys with the index fingers of both hands, but, on consideration, crossed the rest out. He was learning that the best answers were brief. To matter-of-fact questions, factual answers were required, of course. But with questions of the heart, my father was realizing, it was best to be a bit enigmatic.

In matters of the heart, my father already had some experience of his own. He had been involved in a love affair or two, and his heart had been broken. He had observed envy and jealousies cause rifts within his own family. He himself had been the victim of betrayal by a friend. He was no Solomon, he knew, but he felt confident and stimulated. And he felt the first stirrings of what soon would become a new novel moving within him.

The envelope immediately announced itself as different from most of the others that crossed my father's desk. For one thing, it was neatly typed – whereas most he received were handwritten, often crudely so, and in a mixture of English and Yiddish – and addressed fully to Yenta Schmegge/The Wisdom of Solomon, *The Jewish World* and the complete address. Of even more interest was the return address: Prof. M. E. Bell, Department of Sociology and Anthropology, University of Ohio, Columbus, Ohio. Columbus, my father knew, was some one hundred and fifty miles away. He examined the envelope front and back and slit it open with interest.

The letter was addressed not to "esteemed editor" or "worthy Yenta Schmegge," but to "My dear Mrs. Schmegge (or is it Miss?)." Now my father really was interested.

Allow me to introduce myself. My name is

*Madelaine Bell. I'm an assistant professor of anthro-
pology here at the University of Ohio, in Columbus.
Some of your columns have been forwarded to me by a
friend in Cleveland, with rough English translations.*

*I'm particularly interested in the letter from the
woman who was in love with the Indian man. Do you
recall it? I believe it was one of the early letters, and
your reply was indeed Solomonic. I'd very much like to
know what course this woman followed. Do you know
how I can get in touch with her? I'd very much appreciate any help you can give me.*

My father, flabbergasted, paused in his reading to
rub his eyes. Then he continued:

*As it happens, I will be in Cleveland next week for
several days. May I call you at The World? I realize
'Schmegge' may be a pseudonym, but I will call and ask
for you and hope for the best.*

Until then, my very best regards.

The signature intrigued my father. It was just the
name, "Madelaine Bell," with no title, neither "Professor" nor "Miss" nor "Mrs." Bell, he knew, could be an
English name, or it could be a shortened, Anglicized
version of a Jewish name like Belzburg or Belowitz. In
New York, he knew a number of Jewish men who called
themselves Bell. He looked closer at the signature. The
hand was feminine, yet clear and somehow bold, he
thought. He imagined it was the signature of a woman
who was independent – a professor! – who would yield
to no man on matters of principle yet might happily
yield to the pressure of arms and lips. This was exactly
the sort of woman he himself was seeking. He read the
letter again and a third time, and studied the signature

further. He imagined the author of this letter was an attractive woman – but not wildly attractive – with long brown wavy hair and intelligent eyes that could hold and return a gaze. Assistant professor meant that she could not be too old, and he imagined she would be no more than thirty, perhaps younger.

Of course, what would such a woman see in a man who had dropped out of school after the fifth grade, whose education was mostly self-acquired? A man who fabricated letters for a newspaper column of dubious value? A man who she thought was a woman!

My father shook his head and chided himself for his vanity, laughed at himself. Then he took a look at the date on the letter: it had been written on a Thursday. His eyes flicked to the calendar on the wall above the city desk: it was Tuesday, next week already. He went to the front office and told them he might be receiving a call, and if so to put it through immediately. Should he be unavailable for any reason, ask the caller to come down to the paper and ask for him.

Madelaine Bell turned out to be very close to my father's ideal. She was attractive – but not wildly so – with long brown hair much as he'd imagined, except that it was done up neatly in what my father thought was called a French roll. She had an aquiline nose and dark, intelligent eyes, but her thick eyeglasses masked the intent of her look. She was shorter than my father liked, but well-built, and very well dressed in a brown tweed suit, something my father had never seen on a woman. She was, he guessed, about thirty-five, just a few years older than my father. She wore no makeup or jewelry, including no wedding or engagement ring, but her fingernails, he noticed, were long and well cared for, and covered with a purplish-red polish. She didn't look or sound even remotely Jewish.

They sat across from each other in a delicatessen a block away from *The World's* offices, cups of tea in front of them.

"You really thought I was a woman," my father repeated, still amazed.

"You're very convincing," Professor Bell said.

"So convincing as to fool even someone as learned as you, a professor of anthropology! I'm pleased to know that."

The professor explained her interest in the correspondent in love with the Indian. She was involved in a study of the integration of immigrant Jews into American society. Intermarriage between races and faiths of course played a large part. "This woman is exactly the sort of person I'm most interested in. I don't have to tell you the symbolic value of her predicament. In love with an Indian, an original inhabitant of this land. Then there's the Lost Tribe element, the possibility that, in terms of both faith and ethnicity, there is no actual intermarriage. This is invaluable. It could be emblematic for my entire study." After a moment, when my father didn't immediately reply, she added: "And the man's desire to study Judaism, to return to roots he didn't even know he had..."

My father had thought hard about what to tell this woman. Much as he hated to lie, it was unthinkable to admit the fabrication. "I'm sorry to say I can't really help you," he began reluctantly. "The woman wrote no more than what we printed. There was no name on the letter, no return address on the envelope."

"And she hasn't been in touch again?" Madelaine Bell asked hopefully.

"No." After a moment, my father added: "It's been almost four months now, so it's doubtful she will. Who knows what may have become of her?"

"Ah," Professor Bell said. "I would dearly love to interview her." She took off her eyeglasses and gently rubbed the bridge of her nose with her thumb and forefinger, a gesture my father found endearing. When she removed her hand, her eyes, a lighter shade of brown than he had first thought, were warm and inviting. "I wonder if I could impose upon you for a favour?"

"If I can be of service, of course."

"Perhaps you could insert a sentence or two in your column inquiring as to this woman's whereabouts, 'will the woman who wrote the letter on,' I'm sorry, I've forgotten the date, 'will the woman who wrote about her love affair with the Indian man please be in contact...' Something along those lines. Would that be possible?"

"Ah," my father said. Professor Bell had not yet put her glasses back on and he found himself gazing into those warm brown eyes. He felt a moment of panic, as if he were being drawn into those pools of liquid, chocolatey brown, where he would surely drown, but it quickly passed. What harm could such a subterfuge do – other, of course, than to compound the original fabrication? Heshberg, if he even noticed, would find it amusing.

In matters of the heart, my father found, each situation was different. His experience was useless for the situation he soon found himself in.

After some weeks had passed, he was able to imagine writing this letter:

Esteemed Yenta Schmegge,

I find myself unexpectedly in need of your sage advice. I'm enmeshed in an impossible love affair. In fact, I have inextricably entangled myself in a web of deception for which I have less and less stomach every day. The Americans have a phrase for it: 'painting oneself into a corner.'

I am a young man from a good Jewish home. Our family was not religious – I would characterize myself as an agnostic – but Jewishness, if not Judaism, is important to me. Yet I am involved with a Gentile woman, a shiksa, *for whom ethnicity and faith are merely subjects of interest, to be examined and studied rather than adhered to.*

She is a professional woman, a woman of learning, for whom education is of the highest importance. I have very little formal education, though I have done much to improve myself. She is part of a profession that follows a strict code of ethical conduct, that draws a sharp distinction between theory and data. I follow a trade that has high ideals but is essentially amoral.

I love this woman and we are involved in a passionate affair that has gone beyond my wildest dreams. But, in order to advance this affair, I resorted to a number of falsehoods; now, to preserve the affair, I must pile falsehood upon falsehood. There is, I fear, a void at the centre. It is only a matter of time, I'm certain, until this woman, who is no fool, will see through the facade I've erected.

So, I implore and beseech you, tell me, dear, wise Yenta Schmegge, what am I to do?

My father had not really written the letter, but the situation and the question were real enough.

He considered the question, and the one contained

in a letter which had come that day, a real question, in a real letter, from a real reader: "My husband beats me and the children. What should I do?"

He had been sitting at his desk in *The World* newsroom for an hour or more thinking of how to answer this question. It was late, and the newsroom was deserted. There was a bottle of whisky in the bottom drawer of his desk. He opened the drawer, took out the bottle and a small glass and poured himself a drink.

The only answer my father could think of for either dilemma – his own and that of his distressed correspondent – was the one he had written so often in the newspaper: "Follow your heart." In the dim light of the empty newsroom, the inadequacy of the answer – and its falsity – loomed enormous.

A False Moustache

In 1924, when my father came back to New York from Cleveland, he moved uptown to Harlem, where he hoped to find independence.

For several years after dropping out of school at thirteen, my father had knocked around, working at a variety of jobs, usually taking a night class of some sort at the same time from the *Arbeiter Ring*, the Workman's Circle, an organization that sought to bring education and culture to the Jewish immigrants, and travelling some. A problem with his feet allowed him to avoid service in the Great War that raged all over Europe, including the area where he'd been born. This had prevented him from having to put his beliefs in pacifism to the test. Instead of taking up arms, he'd served his country by working on a farm, something he already had some experience with.

Afterwards, he went west, and he had just spent almost four years on a small Yiddish newspaper in Cleveland learning the craft he would earn his living by for the next forty. He liked to tell me, years later, that he would often dream, in the cold rooming-house attic he'd shared with a mouse he called *Maleka*, of returning to the city he'd once thought didn't have room for him, the city of his father's and brother's friends and influence, their reputation, like a bright morning star, burning on the horizon, forcing men to lift their heads and see.

In those days, with the Great War still seeming to reverberate in the air above the city like a subway train that has rumbled out of sight but not hearing, Harlem was already beginning to make the change that was to plunge it into the new world. The handsome brownstones that lined 125th Street and its dissecting avenues were starting the painful process of transforming themselves into neat, genteel boarding houses, like capped teeth in a once proud mouth – the smile still warm, but no longer glittering. My father took a room on the second floor of a Lexington Avenue house, just south of 124th Street, that had once belonged to a lawyer with Tammany connections. The lawyer had died in debt and now his solemn parlor was the domain of an aunt who had only her wits and boarders to keep her together. The room was clean, with a scrubbed window behind starched white curtains looking out on the avenue and one slim slice of Mount Morris Park, two blocks west, that wasn't cut off by the buildings across the way. North of 125th, where the roots were deeper or the money of better quality, my father didn't know which, there were still families with servants living in the pillared, imposing brownstones, and from his window, on warm afternoons, he could watch the black nursemaids, who lived far south of the pleasant street, strolling with their charges to the park, where they would sit on benches and watch the children play in the sun. He paid twelve dollars a week, and that included coffee and rolls in the morning, dinner sharply at six. When he worked the night shift, as he often did, his landlady packed him a wholesome lunch.

There was no mouse in the room on Lexington Avenue and, even though the subway ride downtown to East Broadway took almost an hour, my father enjoyed living there, far from the sights and smells that meant something different entirely. And his enjoyment was enhanced somewhat when, after several weeks, he ran into Louis Shmelke in the hall outside his room.

"Shmelke," my father said, surprised and pleased, still new enough in his surroundings to be lonely, "what brings you here?"

"I have to go," Shmelke shrugged, gesturing towards the toilet at the end of the hall. At the other end, my father could see, a door hung open, the door to the room where, he believed, a travelling salesman with a lingerie firm resided. Or had.

"So go," my father said, moving out of the lean man's way, "but step in on your way back and begin the process again."

A minute later, they were lifting their water glasses to the memory of Cleveland. "May that infernal lake from which blows that infernal cold wind overspill its shores and swallow the infernal city up," Shmelke said, licking his lips with a peculiar slapping sound, like small waves on stones. He swallowed the whisky with a single gulp.

He was a tall, fleshless man with ears like mushrooms springing out of moist earth, fond of suits a size too large, as if he expected suddenly to put on weight. His lips were the size and colour of the patches on a worn inner tube. He was altogether the most homely man my father had ever known, quite an accomplishment in a world populated by men who worked too hard or kept their heads on too lofty planes to be physically vain.

"It was my partner, that infernal rascal Goldblatt, who forced me to descend," Shmelke said in explanation for his presence, both in the city and these modest surroundings. He was a humourless, literal man whose command of his second language was not quite up to his reach.

"The ticket selling?" my father inquired after a moment's thought. They had not been friends, by any means, but they'd frequented the same café in Cleveland, a gathering spot for poets, newspapermen, actors, artists, musicians and hangers-on, and he'd known of half a dozen different ventures in which Shmelke was involved. "Artists' representative" was what he liked to call himself; press agent was closer to the truth; ticket agent was, in fact, what he was the last time my father had heard.

"Let me tell you, that was no sofa on roses, that expedition. It was a service, a struggle of love, something to do for the people, you know what I mean, Morgenstern? You think I could make a dollar on a thing like that?"

"Would I argue with you?" my father asked. He poured another two fingers of whisky into the dusty glasses.

"My partner, what a *shlimazel*, a head for business he had on his shoulders as big as this." Shmelke held up his thumb, examined it critically then replaced it with his pinky. "As big as this, no bigger." He gulped down the whisky with a rubbery slap. "We had these tickets, this big order, something really expressive, for opera, Caruso, no, not him, but someone just as infamous, and it brought in a lot of money. A lot? It made me enervated having that much money so close. And was I right?"

He slapped his narrow forehead with the palm of his hand. "That infermal *shmegegge* had a chance – a *chance*, he called it, a hole in the ground would be more like it – to buy up a whole theatre for Gilbert and Sullivan, so he used all the money from the opera tickets. The whole cat and caboodle."

"Sounds like a smart move," my father said naively.

"A smart move? Sure, like suicide is smart for the widow and the dolphins." Shmelke glared at my father as if he were in the company of a fool. My father tipped the bottle over the glasses.

"So there comes the man from the opera saying where's the money from the tickets? So what do we say?"

"Tomorrow?" my father offered.

Shmelke peered at him with skeptical admiration. "Sure, tomorrow, that's context. But what happens after tomorrow?"

"Gilbert and Sullivan is sold?"

"Morgenstern, no offensive, but you and my infermal partner Goldblatt would be sweethearts, regular darlings, newlyweds you could be."

"You couldn't sell Gilbert and Sullivan?"

Shmelke's watery eyes rolled up and almost disappeared into his eyelids. "Morgenstern, you can *always* sell Gilbert and Sullivan. In Cleveland, Gilbert could be elected mayor, Sullivan the governor of Ohio, maybe."

"So what's the problem?"

"Problem? Who said anything about a problem? Morgenstern, you surprise me. *Problem?* What a cryptic. No problem, believe me. The Gilbert and Sullivan money goes to the opera and that accounting is closed, the book is finished, *kaput.* A little inconsideration, maybe, when the Gilbert and Sullivan cancels and there's the refunds to make, but a *problem? Noooo.* "

Shmelke glared at my father, challenging him, and, though he was tempted to say he didn't understand, my father held his tongue. After that, the two men saw each other often, in the hallway outside the toilet, rather than at the dinner table, as my father was then working nights, and often they would share a glass of whisky in my father's room, occasionally in Shmelke's. The man did not bathe often and there was an odour in his room that my father found worth the price of his whisky to avoid.

It was spring when my father moved into the room in Harlem, and the city was opening itself up for him the way leaves and blossoms open themselves up to the insects that float on the warm breezes of April and May. The Jewish life of New York was rich and exciting in those days, its theatre vigorous, its literature strong and searching, its artists bold and sensitive with a freedom growing out of a new sense of purpose after a hundred years or more of lying low. There were half a dozen Yiddish dailies in the city then – his father was editor of one of them, *The Morning Journal*, and his older brother Sam worked for another, *The Day* – and the competition between them was fierce, their pages filled with essays on the arts and philosophy, criticism, Talmudic debate, humour, advice on everything from self-improvement to affairs of the heart and body, along with news of the far-flung community and the world at large that owed as much, in its style and presentation, to Hearst and Pulitzer as it did to Spinoza and the learned rabbis of Poland and Russia. My father was a news writer, not an essayist, toiling, like his brother, for *The Day*, but he loved the company of the great men he drank coffee with in the cafeteria at the corner of East Broadway and Rutgers Street and at the Café Royale on Second Avenue, in the heart of the Yiddish theatre district known as the Jewish Rialto, where the lights burned all through the night like beacons.

Sometimes, he would encounter Shmelke there. The tall, skinny man with the pennant ears had secured a position as press agent to a rabbinical council and was also doing publicity work for a hospital in the Bronx. But his heart and soul belonged to the arts and he often could be found in the evenings at the Café Royale and other warm, bright rooms that sparkled through the grey streets of the Lower East Side like fireflies. There were often actors still in makeup and costume, sometimes outlandish costume, at the café, and Shmelke, with his ill-fitting suits and clownish face, could easily have been one of them, my father thought.

"Morgenstern, Morgenstern, join us. Sit down, my friend. Combine with me a drink. You know Rubenstein and Pashka?"

"Of course." My father sat, smiling. Despite the invitation, he knew he would pay for the whisky he ordered.

"Rubenstein, the steamed violinist, and Pashka, the clammed dramatist. Morgenstern, the novelist and poet."

My father knew both men – one a teacher of music at a Hebrew school, the other a stagehand at the Yiddish Art Theatre across the street – and the conversation was good, the evening warm. He lingered, although it was late. Shmelke and he rode home together on the subway.

"Come in, have a drink," Shmelke begged. "I've got something to show you."

My father's curiosity was stronger than his tiredness and he followed the bobbing head with its ballast ears into the cluttered room, rich with the smell of socks. On the rumpled bed, there was a peaked white cap like those he had seen the black nursemaids in the park wearing. Shmelke snatched it up and twirled it on a finger, grinning darkly.

There was a bottle of cheap rye on the dresser and my father poured two glasses.

"You should see her, Morgenstern," Shmelke said.

"An angel, a dark angel, like devil's food cake, like an animal of the night."

My father was moved by the intensity and clarity of Shmelke's description. He swallowed his drink and took out a cigarette.

"You've had this woman here? In your room?"

"Right here," Shmelke grinned, patting the twisted bedclothes. "Why not?" He tossed the cap carelessly onto the bed, shrugging his shoulders. "What do I care what people think?"

"Very commendable, my friend, but does that include our landlady?"

The rubbery lips smacked at the rim of his glass. "Depression, depression, Morgenstern, is the soul of valour." He winked.

"And the girl? She's nice?"

Shmelke laughed, a cackling that reminded my father of the chickens that used to share the kitchen of his mother's farmhouse in the winter, years before, when he'd been a boy in Galicia. "Nice, what's nice? To the Café Royale, I don't intend to bring her. *Here*, she's nice." He pointed to the bed.

"Is it wise, though, one of those girls?" my father asked cautiously.

"Morgenstern, of you I'm shameless." Shmelke fixed him with a stern gaze, the rims of his elephant ears reddening slightly. "A man like you, a spigot."

During that first year of his return to the city, when my father was firmly establishing himself as a newspaper-man, and some time before he would meet my mother, he had love affairs of his own, great friendships, nights of talk and whisky and coffee that lasted till dawn, though his lack of formal schooling always made him feel a little inadequate in intellectual circles. He believed in free love, or thought he did, until my mother came into his life and he changed his mind on that subject quickly and entirely. He was active in the Jewish Writers Guild, which got its start at the same time as the Newspaper Guild but soon outstripped its English language rival. He got a raise. And one night, in late summer, he was witness to a murder and wrote a story that made an impression on his editors.

My father had an interest in labour, but there already was a labour editor on the paper, a stern old man who had been a scholar and teacher in the old country and who wrote with the grace of an albatross. When this man, Jaffe, was busy, my father was often pressed into service to help him if there was a conflict, and on an evening in September he went to cover a meeting of a group of garment cutters who were organizing themselves.

The meeting was in a small kosher restaurant on Seventeenth Street, between Third and Fourth Avenues. It had been warm when my father left Harlem that afternoon and he had not worn a coat, but as darkness fell it turned cold and a stiff wind was sending newspapers skittering along the empty street as he walked towards the restaurant, the collar of his suit jacket turned up against his neck. A man in a lumberjack's plaid shirt stood lounging against the plate glass of the restaurant, a toothpick in his mouth.

"Morgenstern," the man said.

"Schechter, hello, you look like you're ready for heavy labour."

"I'm glad you could come," Schechter said. "Those shits at the English papers, they don't pay any attention." He was a big man with a sensitive face who drank coffee occasionally in the Café Royale with a thin actress he was in love with. In Lithuania, my father knew, he had studied to be a doctor, but now he worked in the garment district, his quick fingers racing over patterns with a pair of scissors. He shrugged his massive shoulders. "Heavy labour, sure. This is no kids' stuff, you know."

There had been a strike in one of the sweatshops that abounded like blossoms off the stem of lower Seventh Avenue, and then, mysteriously, there was a fire in the building and two of the organizers of the strike were arrested, charged with arson. Schechter himself had avoided the police only by accident. The fire was the work of gangsters, everyone knew, but fighting back was no easy matter.

My father lit a cigarette and glanced up the street. On the corner, a light burned in a newsstand but the other shops were dark. He would have liked to stand outside and chat with Schechter but it was cold and he opened the door of the restaurant. "See you inside." As he moved into the warmth and the clatter of voices from the already crowded tables, he heard the sound of a car on the street but thought nothing of it. The shot rang out just as the door was clicking shut behind him and it didn't register immediately; even when the glass shattered and Schechter's shoulders crashed through towards him, he didn't fully understand what had happened. Then there was confusion, shouting, a man rushing past him, jostling him, knocking him sideways, and he cut his hand on a piece of glass and found himself on his knees, staring into Schechter's wide open eyes. What he remembered most of that moment, even many years later, was the lack of surprise in them.

His hand was still bleeding when he got home, hours later, although he had tied a handkerchief around it. Taking notes, telephoning, typing his story, there had been no chance for the wound even to begin to glaze over. The handkerchief was stiff with congealing blood and my father was attempting to take it off, his head lowered, as he climbed the stairs, and he bumped into Shmelke, who was standing at the top of the steps.

"That woman, she's here, what should I do?" Shmelke said breathlessly. His massive ears were tinged with red along the rims like warning signs, and his lips seemed bluer than usual.

"So?" my father said, elbowing past him. "Excuse me. What woman is that?"

He went to the bathroom and snapped on the light, discarding the bloody handkerchief in the toilet.

"You don't understand," Shmelke whined. He was standing right behind him, his face pressed close to my father's shoulder. "She's right here, in my infermal room."

"What's to understand?" my father said. He turned on the cold water tap and plunged his hand into the lukewarm stream. "You should be congratulated, Shmelke. A charming young lady, visiting you here in your own room, and at this hour, no less. Wonderful. You are to be congratulated and I do congratulate you. And wish you good luck." He was filled with the events of the evening and would have liked nothing better than to share them, again, with anyone interested, even Shmelke, but the man's single-mindedness irritated him.

"*Morgenstern*, sometimes I wonder how such a dope can manage to climb the stairs, let alone turn the knob on the door." He pulled his head back when he saw the expression that flashed across my father's face. "You'll excuse me, I didn't mean to defend. But this woman, she's got me in such a tizzle. This *svartze*."

"Oh, that woman," my father said, his eyes widening. "She's here?"

"Here? That's nothing. Here I could live with. It's who she's got with her that sends shavings up my spine."

"Her boyfriend?" My father turned off the water and held his hand up to the light to examine the cut. It wasn't very deep but the glass had severed a big vein, an artery perhaps, and the blood wouldn't stop seeping out. "Her husband? Her mother?"

"Worse," Shmelke said gloomily. His belligerence had suddenly faded and he stared at the raw wound on my father's hand as if he were considering how a similar gash would look on his throat. "What happened to your hand?"

"It's nothing," my father said. All of a sudden, he wanted to speak no more of it. All he wanted was to go to his room, drink a whisky and lie on his bed in the dark, where he knew the sound of shattering glass would reverberate in his ears all morning long. "What is it, Shmelke?"

"She's pregnant."

"Ah, so that's it." My father turned back to his hand, wrapping toilet paper around it till it was bulky as a crumpled package.

Shmelke observed this in silence, pursing his lips like water wings bobbing in a rough sea. "You know, maybe, a doctor?" he blurted out finally.

My father looked up from his hand into Shmelke's face and was washed with a wave of disgust. He remembered the blank, stoical eyes of Schecter staring up at him and he felt, suddenly, very tired.

"Sure, sure," he said. He brushed past Shmelke. "I'll see in the morning." He walked down the hall.

"And Morgenstern?" There was a plaintiveness in Shmelke's voice my father had never heard before and it made him stop, his hand on the knob of his own door.

"Yes?"

"You could talk to her, maybe?"

My father turned around. "Now?"

"Sure, now. She's in my room, waiting. She won't go. All night, practically, she's here. She won't give me any peace. And Mrs. Lowe..." He nodded towards the stairs.

"Waiting for what?" my father asked. "Talk to her about what?"

"Tell her about the doctor you know. Tell her about how safe and sure this doctor is, how they take preclusions and it's no more than getting your tinsels out, just a little cut and..."

My father didn't wait for him to finish. He went down the hall and into Shmelke's room without knocking. The woman was sitting on the bed, her knees together and her hands clasped on them like a school-child waiting to receive her lesson. "Hello," my father said. "My name is Harry Morgenstern. I live here, down the hall."

The woman looked up at him and blinked. She was a small, very dark girl, hardly out of her teens, with a pointy chin and shoulders that didn't seem to matter. Her face was so dark, my father couldn't clearly make out her features, but she seemed pleasant enough, though hardly pretty. There was a blue kerchief with little white flowers on her head. "Where's Louis?" she demanded. Her voice was small but strong, like a rain that seems innocent enough but wets you through.

"I'm right here, my little flower," Shmelke said from the doorway. "My friend Morgenstern, the novelist, he's a man of the world. Believe me, to him this is nothing. He's seen this sort of thing dozens of times." He made a snapping motion with his fingers but they wouldn't connect and there was only a rasping sound. "It's only a triffle."

My father sat on the bed beside the woman. She glared at him but, after a moment, her gaze softened.

"Why don't you leave us for a moment, Shmelke? There's a bottle in my room. Help yourself." He had to fumble in his pocket with his left hand for the key. They waited until the door had closed, Shmelke's footsteps sounded in the hall, and another door could be heard opening, then closing. Then my father and the black woman looked at each other again.

"He's very stupid, our friend," my father said simply.

"Ain't no friend of mine, not any more," the woman said. "But stupid, that's for sure."

"I'm not the man of the world Shmelke says I am," my father said, smiling, "but I can see trouble."

"I've got plenty to see." The skin on the woman's cheekbones was so tight it glistened.

"What's your name?"

"Adrianne."

"That's nice," my father said. "That's a nice name."

The woman began to cry, lifting her hands to cover her face, the sobs coming soft but steady for over a minute while my father looked away and said nothing. When the sobbing became inaudible, he said: "You don't want him."

"I know that, mister. I *acted* the fool, but I ain't no fool."

"What *do* you want?"

"I don't know. I came here thinking I wanted one thing, but now I don't know."

"A doctor?"

"A butcher, you mean? No, thank you, mister. I don't want no coat hangers and razor blades in me. Bad enough what I let get into me in the first place."

"Take it easy," my father said. "I'm not Shmelke. I just asked."

"I'm sorry," Adrianne said.

They were quiet for a moment. My father looked idly at his hand. A muted red stain was beginning to spread through the toilet paper wrapping like fog spreading through the streets in the Cleveland evening, what seemed now like a lifetime ago. "Does Shmelke have any money?" he asked.

"That man?" She snorted. "He spends every cent on whisky and such with his fancy friends downtown."

"I can give you some money, if it would help."

"It would," Adrianne said simply. It was clear she wasn't asking, but she wouldn't refuse.

My father stood up. "What about him?"

The woman shook her head sadly. The whites of her eyes were pink now, and her face was blurred, as if it had let go of the bones beneath the skin. "I don't want to see that poor excuse again."

"Wait here," my father said. He went across the hall to his room, hesitating just for a second before opening the door. Shmelke was sitting on the chair beside the bed, an empty glass in his hand. His reddened ears seemed to flap, like flags of distress.

My father knelt beside the bed and took some money from its hiding place in his suitcase. There wasn't much.

"What are you doing?" Shmelke asked. His voice was tiny, like that of a punished child.

"Saving your life," my father said.

"What do you mean?"

"What the thunder do you think I mean?" my father snapped.

I know his temper, and I can imagine the way his eyes must have darkened, his moustache bristling. "Her father and brothers would kill you. I'm buying that off. But there's one condition. You can't let them find you.

You'll have to leave."

Shmelke was speechless, but when my father glared at him, showing no sign of relenting, he said finally: "I'll go tomorrow."

"Tonight would be better, but it's your neck."

"I'll go early. There are things I have to do, circumcisions I have to attend to..."

"You know I don't mean just from here. I mean from New York."

"I know," Shmelke said bitterly. "I'm not stupid."

My father started for the door. Blood was beginning to drip on the bills he held in his bandaged hand.

"I'll pay you back," Shmelke said.

"If you want."

"I pay my debts, Morgenstern. I don't like to be a belcher."

My father shut the door and stood in the hall for a moment, staring at the money in his bloody hand. It was all he had, but that didn't mean anything.

The following year, my father was keeping company with a woman who might have become my mother, had he been a little less demanding. Years later, he liked to tell stories about this woman, whose name was Debora, and kid my mother that he had settled for the daughter of a fanatic when he could have had a physician for a father-in-law.

My father was living in Coney Island at that time, in a tiny apartment not far from the slightly larger one he and my mother would share during their first few years together, but Debora's family was one of those that still maintained a handsome brownstone just north of 125th Street, a home with rich carpets on the parquet floors and servants living in the coach house. So, although he no longer lived there, he was a frequent visitor to Harlem, and he had occasion, once or twice, to pass Adrianne on the street or in the park. She had gone south, to stay with relatives, and had had her child. It was still there, with an aunt, and she was back, living with a man who fixed shoes in a small shop on 125th a few blocks east and tending the infant of a white family, taking it in its stroller for airings in the park, where the sun filtering through the newly opened leaves dappled the grass and benches with blotches of light and dark like footprints in the snow. My father, running across her with the stroller parked beside her bench, her uniform crisp and neat on her small, unremarkable form, paused to admire the infant, inquire about the other and shake his head sadly.

"It don't bear thinking about much," Adrianne said, and he agreed. There was no mention of Shmelke.

One Saturday afternoon in August, my father and Debora took a shortcut through the park on the way to Columbia University, where they planned to attend a free concert. As they walked, my father was suddenly arrested by a strange sight. A tall man wearing an overcoat was sitting on a bench under a chestnut tree, his ears big as the leaves hanging above his head. The overcoat was buttoned, although it was a warm day, and its collar was raised. The man wore dark glasses and there was a shapeless moustache over his bluish lips.

My father put his hand on Debora's arm and steered her to a bench some fifty feet beyond the one where the man with the moustache sat, but facing it. "What is it?" Debora asked. My father shooshed her with a finger to his nose. He crossed his legs and lit a cigarette.

Several people passed by, including a black nursemaid with a stroller and two small boys in short pants in tow. She wore her hair in braids and her silvery voice rose through the air like a bird's song as she chastised the lagging boys. They passed on, towards the far side of the park.

Before my father's cigarette was half gone, the man with the moustache, who had been nervously turning his head to and fro, became aware of the couple watching him and he bolted to his feet and began to hurry away.

"Wait here," my father said. He had to run to catch up with the tall man's quick strides.

"Shmelke."

"For God's sake, Morgenstern, my life is in jalopy. Keep your voice down."

My father took him by the arm and gestured around. They were alone on a path that led through a small clump of trees. On the street, a hundred yards beyond, a fire engine raced by, its bell clanging. "Look, there's not a soul in sight. You're in no danger."

"I can't be too careless," Shmelke said.

They sat down on a bench.

"That false moustache is ridiculous," my father said. "Why didn't you grow a real one?"

"I was going to, but my wife didn't like it. It scritched," he said with disgust, as if describing some loathsome insect crawling on his face.

"Your wife?" my father asked.

"In Dayton."

"I heard you went back to Cleveland."

"Are you crazy, Morgenstern? Only to get some clothes."

"And in Dayton?"

Shmelke's lean shoulders had to struggle against the weight of the overcoat to produce a satisfied shrug.

"Not so bad, not so bad as you might think. I'm in business there, producing plays, bringing artists in, musicians, travelling shows. Let me tell you, Morgenstern, what Dayton has for culture, you could put in there." He raised a thumb, examined it critically, then replaced it with a pinky. "No more than that. In Dayton, they got taste in their elbow."

"And you're married?"

"Well...not exactly married," Shmelke shrugged again, the tips of his ears flaring. "Bedthroned. The happy day is next week."

"And what brings you here, Shmelke? Taking your life in your hands."

Shmelke sighed deeply, the breath rattling through his chest like a cold wind through dead branches, and the brown caterpillar beneath his nose wiggled, one end hanging loose. "There was...there was something I wanted to see. With my own eyes."

"Yes?"

"I wanted to see if...my wife, the woman to whom I'm intended, that is, Hindel, she would like to have children."

"So?" my father said. He took out a cigarette and lit it, wishing he had a bottle so he and Shmelke could share their ritual drink.

"So," Shmelke said, spreading his arms, "so I'm not such a thing of beauty, you know, but...and Hindel, well, she is a wonderful woman, but..." His voice trailed off and he looked over my father's shoulder, as if for inspiration in the trees.

"But what does all this have to do with your coming here?" my father asked.

"I wanted to see if...you know, Morgenstern, if the child looks like me."

"It doesn't have a moustache, if that's what you

mean," my father said. Immediately, he regretted having said that. If there was one thing he had learned in the long years it had taken him to come this far, it was not to hurt people, that it usually came back to him if he did.

Shmelke took off his dark glasses and my father saw there were tears in his grey, almost colourless eyes. There was no surprise in them, though, as if the man who possessed them had become accustomed to rebuff. He clasped my father's hand and squeezed it, and for the first time in many months the place where it had been cut began to hurt.

"Is it so wrong, Morgenstern, for a man to want to see his own springoff? His own child? His own flesh and bones?"

"No," my father said. He disengaged his hand and got to his feet. Debora would be wondering where he had gotten to.

Shmelke made a little sound in his throat and lowered his head, looking to his oversized feet for an answer that had eluded him so far in Cleveland and Dayton and would not easily be found here, either downtown on East Broadway or uptown in Harlem, where some people said the air was thinner.

My father didn't mention the money still owing, and neither did Shmelke.

Feathers and Blood

One day in the spring of 1927, on the same day that Lindbergh was crossing the Atlantic, a young woman by the name of Rebeccah Kristol sent my father a letter from Cleveland with the message: "Now."

At that time, my father was already firmly established as a reporter on *The Day*, the Yiddish-language daily that sent its messages of the toils and joys of Jewish life in New York from the Lower East Side throughout the city and even into the countryside beyond the rivers, and was several years into what would be a lifetime career. In a couple more years, he would meet my mother and everything would change for him. But already there had been a few women in his life, women who, in the telling later, became blurred, indistinct as buildings viewed through fog, perhaps to spare my mother, perhaps merely so that my father, who enjoyed telling stories of his youth, could keep some small pieces of it private, for his own, like good luck coins fingered and shiny in his pocket. He never said so, but I suspect Rebeccah Kristol was one of those coins, not just a friend from the old days in Cleveland, as he described her when he told the story, but one of the women who had been part of his life in those years before my mother, before the time when my sisters and I were given our chance to be.

Rebeccah was a strong woman, my father used to tell us, a determined woman with ideas of her own and the courage to put some – if not all – of them into effect. She was a drinker and a smoker, mildly shocking behaviour for a woman in those days, at least in some strata of society – even the society my father and Rebeccah inhabited – as well as a freethinker and free lover, an anarchist follower of Anna Goldman, a dabbler in vegetarianism, frequenter of cafés and theatres, friend of artists and writers, which is how my father, who was a writer himself and part of the Bohemian café circle, such as it was in Cleveland, came to know her.

The one photograph he had of her, one of several brittle, yellow tintypes from his early days that could be found scattered in among the more abundant family portraits and snapshots of my mother's childhood and pictures of her and my father as a young couple and we children that filled a shoebox my mother kept in a dresser drawer, revealed Rebeccah as clearly possessed of those qualities of character my father ascribed to her but contained not a hint of the predilections and interests. She is one of only three women in the portrait filled with men, a solemn, formal study of activity suddenly arrested in the newsroom of *The Day*, circa 1930, more than a decade before my birth. He himself is sitting at a desk in the pose I like best to remember him in, hands poised over the keys of an ancient stand-up typewriter, head slightly lowered, moustache bristling, cigarette dangling from a mouth pursed with concentration, his hair only just beginning to thin, still rich and black. The other men and one of the women are captured in similar freezes, at typewriters or bent over teletype machines, reading, one or two on the telephone, a few with their backs to the camera, and there is a sense of busyness and purpose to the scene that is unmarred by the other two women, who stand, stiff and vigilant at either end of the room, like prim bookends.

Rebeccah is the one on the right, in a long black skirt and ruffled white blouse with a bow at the throat, her dark hair in a severe bun, her face partially shielded by thick-rimmed glasses. She was, at the time the photograph was taken, less than thirty, but there is a sort of agelessness about her face, her strong, well-defined features facing the camera with intelligent interest neither youthfully beautiful nor showing any of the decay of years. Her eyes seem to sparkle, and her mouth and chin are firm, as if they were being held into the wind. But her clothes, her hairstyle, even the rigid way she holds her arms by her sides, one hand seeming to be smoothing a pleat in her skirt, all point to a manner of conventionality that runs against the way my father had described her.

"She was a changed woman when she came to New York," my father said as he showed me the picture, anticipating my thought. "Whatever happened to her in that love affair, in that marriage, in that boat ride, it turned her inside out." He carefully deposited the photograph back into its protective envelope, along with a few others from the same era, and looked at me. "She never lost her intelligence, of course, or her taste, but her curiosity about the world shrivelled up, and she became the sort of person she had always disliked, a closed sort of person. As if she were making up for something."

All of that, my father used to say when he told the story, was so much more perplexing because of the kind of woman she had been, "a woman who" – and here, if they were in the room, my mother and sisters, who were quite a bit older than me, would grimace, my sisters actually groaning – "had all the intellectual and creative abilities and instincts of a man." When she'd sent him that note, he'd kept his promise and gotten her a job, as a bookkeeper at *The Day*, where she would remain all her working life, rising to be chief bookkeeper, the austere, darkly dressed, slightly plump woman with a wart on her nose who would greet me so cheerily on those infrequent occasions when I'd visit my father in his office, where even the air in the newsroom was redolent with the smell of printer's ink wafting in from the black-walled pressroom downstairs. He'd gotten her the job, helped her settle in and been as much of a friend to her as he could. But they'd never been really close again, not close enough for her to go beyond telling him *what* had happened, to *why*.

It began, he knew, when she'd met the man, a salesman who had worked his way up to manager of a small haberdashery on Lake Street in downtown Cleveland, then bought out the widow of the man he'd worked for. His name, my father thought, was Greenspan, although that didn't seem to matter. Nothing about him, my father said, seemed to matter, since the problem was within Rebeccah.

The first time I can recall hearing the story, when I was six or seven, and for several retellings afterwards, my father explained that she had had earlier sweethearts, and that her husband-to-be was jealous. This had "caused problems," my father said with a wink, "but nothing that feminine wiles couldn't cope with." Later, when I was twelve or thirteen, the story changed accordingly, and my father explained the "problem" was that Rebeccah was not a virgin, a condition that was sure to cause displeasure for her husband – "not all husbands," my father added quickly, "but some men care, and this one definitely." And, finally, at some point during the year I went away to college, on one of those short but intense visits home, the story came full cycle, my father relating with head-shaking wonder the facts he had come to know in detail some time later, after she'd come to New York: how, to stave off discovery, she'd planned and carried out the simple subterfuge, as brilliant and easily accomplished as the friend who had coached her had promised. It had gone well, my father said, but afterwards, as the husband lay sleeping, Rebeccah had walked the deck of their honeymoon cruise ship, staring into the dark, impenetrable waves of Lake Erie, and come to some – to my father – inexplicable resolve. She went back to their cabin just for a few minutes, to throw a few things into a suitcase, then she'd hidden in a washroom until the ship docked in fog-shrouded Buffalo and disembarked with the first crowds, losing herself amid the noise and crowds on the dock.

It was sometime soon after that that she'd written the note to my father, the fulfillment of some late-night café pledge he'd made when they'd been close, that when she was ready to leave Cleveland, where some family obligation he was never clear about kept her bound, and escape to New York, where he was now headed, she would let him know and he would help her find a job, help her make what, in those days, and for a woman, was still a difficult passage. The note she sent – and he was sorry, my father always said, he hadn't saved it – didn't have to say more than it did, because he knew from that one word, "Now," all he needed, really: that she was ready to come, that she wanted his help, and more, that it was a cry for help, a signal for freedom.

His name, in fact, was Green*spun*, Aaron Greenspun, whose family had settled in Akron, where an uncle became the first Jew to serve on a city council in Ohio. He had yellow eyes, like a cat's, and Rebeccah, dreaming of them, thought his name should more truly be *Gold*spun, so did it seem those eyes must have been fashioned. He was tall, well built, like a Greek god, Rebeccah told her best friend Belle and the other women she drank coffee with at the café – who pursed their mouths in impressed wonder as they gazed at the rumpled, round-shouldered men arguing at the next table, then giggled at the perceived possibilities – and had only the slightest curved Semitic nose in his otherwise smooth and blandly featured face to betray his origins. He was altogether beautiful, "the most beautiful thing I've ever seen," Rebeccah told her friends, conscious of her choice of words. Her attraction to him frightened her.

They had absolutely nothing in common, shouldn't have even met except there was a family connection, Rebeccah's one weakness. A Greenspun cousin had married a Williams cousin – Williams being Rebeccah's mother's family name, the Americanized version of Wilchevski that her father, Rebeccah's hard-headed, bristly bearded grandfather, had adopted in one of those Ellis Island subterfuges that had smoothed the wrinkles from so many Russian and Polish names. The old man, long dead now, had begun as a peddler but had worked his horse and wagon into a stand, then a small shop, then Williams Brothers, one of Cleveland's better furniture stores, proving his abilities as a merchant and his sagacity, he always claimed, as a name-picker. That side of the family – the store was now run by Rebeccah's uncles Meyer and Robert – seemed to have much in common with the Greenspuns of Akron and their one Cleveland offshoot, all of them prosperous, right-thinking family people who erected big brick houses near the lakefront and gave work to coloured maids who, as Uncle Meyer once explained to Rebeccah, would be

Dave Margoshes

jobless and go hungry otherwise, "which you, I suppose, Miss High And Mighty, would rather see?"

Rebeccah herself was considerably different. She had had the good fortune, she liked to tell her friends, of "marrying smart," referring not to herself but to her mother. Jacob Kristol was a working man and union organizer with rough hands and an intelligence striving to free itself of an inadequate education, not a trader, by any means, but a man who would smile when he saw children stealing apples from a street vendor. He had had three years of school in Russia, then another two in New York's Brownsville, enough to give him sufficient English to go to work, at a factory manufacturing umbrella handles, but the bulk of what he knew of the world came from night school, correspondence courses, workshops put on by the union and a voracious appetite for reading that had made him, in his old age, a favourite of the librarians at the stately Carnegie branch in downtown Cleveland, where he would spend most of his afternoons from the time of his retirement until his death, in the reading room, crumpled over *Crime and Punishment*, which he was reading for the fourth time. He'd come to Cleveland as a young man, on a freight train with a trio of anarchists, to work and help organize the foundry. Then he'd stayed, marrying, as the Williamses always put it, "above his position," and fathering two children, a son who took after his mother's side of the family but died in the war, and a daughter – Rebeccah – who took after him.

Rebeccah's devotion to him was, in some respects, her undoing. Jacob Kristol had married late, so he was already an old man through most of the time his daughter knew him, retired before she was through with school and dead before she had barely reached twenty. But his impact on her was powerful, making her different from most of the girls she went to school with, leaving her bored and dissatisfied with the few boys who were willing to penetrate the veil of sarcasm and feigned intellectualism with which she clothed herself, and she would have liked to have fled from the small city provincialism of Cleveland when she graduated, but her father's failing health kept her at home. Then, when he died, a pledge to him that she would look after her mother, who was also ailing, continued to keep her bound. By this time, she had a job, an apartment and a life of her own, and had discovered the small café society of artists and poets, actors and anarchists who frequented the cluster of cafés and delicatessens along River Avenue on either side of the Rialto Theatre, where touring companies from New York would stage the latest in Yiddish productions.

"You're too good for this narrow stage," one of the actors – a handsome man with a cleft in his chin who went on to have a career in Hollywood under a new name – told her after they'd made love on the mattress of straw-filled ticking in her small, darkly lit loft. "Why don't you come with me?"

"And you'll make me a star?" Rebeccah asked, batting the long, artificially thickened lashes of her large, luminous eyes.

"Seriously," the actor said. "You're too beautiful, too intelligent to let yourself stifle in this ridiculous city where it's always either too hot or too cold."

"And in your bed, the temperature is better controlled?" Rebeccah asked.

My father tried too. "Come with me to New York," he told her when he was getting ready to leave. He had spent almost four years in Cleveland at a small Yiddish newspaper, a worthwhile apprenticeship, and now felt he was ready to go home, and he would have liked to take her with him, this beautiful creature with wild, tangled hair and nicotine and paint stains on her long, delicate fingers, like some sort of souvenir of the great hinterlands across the Hudson River, proof of his passage.

Rebeccah kissed him, gently, like an echo. "You know I can't, Morgenstern," she said. "But I will someday."

"Will you let me know?" my father asked fervently.

"I'll let you know when I'm ready," Rebeccah said.

Before that happened, she met Aaron Greenspun.

Perhaps she'd meant it, always meant to leave, to find a broader world to the east, in New York, where so much of the nightly café talk centred, perhaps even in Paris, where she longed to study art at the Sorbonne, but time passed, her mother lingered, then died, freeing her from her final bond, but still, somehow, she stayed, and before she could muster her energies for that flight, he appeared, changing everything.

It was at a family gathering, the first one of any real consequence since the marriage of the cousins, and he was there, being led through the gauntlet of Williamses by Aunt Ruth, who took Rebeccah fondly by the hand when she came to her.

"And this is Rebeccah, our darling black sheep."

The black sheep was a tag Rebeccah had smilingly endured for years, even before her father's death, but tonight, with her hair in a wooly, swirling halo around her head and dressed all in black, even to her stockings, the tag seemed exceptionally appropriate, and she was radiantly bewitching, a fact that was hardly lost on the tall, handsome man in Aunt Ruth's tow. Nor was her effect on him lost on Rebeccah. They smiled at each other and a current of sexual tension crackled between them like an electric spark running along a twist of broken copper wire.

"The black sheep? More like a black diamond,"

Aaron said, in Yiddish that was almost cultured in its precision.

"Coal, you mean," Rebeccah said. She gave him her most radiant smile, showing all her teeth, and made a noise that was somewhat like a hiss.

"No, no, a sheep, a poor little lamb," Aunt Ruth said, putting her arm around Rebeccah and rocking her gently against her shoulder. "This child just lost her mother, my darling sister, so treat her gently."

"Aunt Ruth, that was almost two years ago."

"And still unmarried. Just a lamb, a poor lost lamb, but a *black* lost lamb, so what's to do with her?"

Aunt Ruth gave both their hands a squeeze and looked from face to face, then seemed to make a decision. "Be nice to each other, children. Rebeccah is a lost black lamb; Aaron is a stranger, a Jew among Jews, of course, but a stranger nonetheless." She moved on, making no indication that he should follow.

Aaron shifted his weight from one lean hip to the other and cleared his throat. If Rebeccah truly was a black sheep, he was a white shepherd, dressed in grey trousers with a sharp crease – just the kind, her father used to say, the bosses use to cut the throat of the working man – and a white linen jacket with an ironed handkerchief in the breast pocket. And his yellow eyes, gazing shyly at her. "A white knight," Rebeccah said.

"Pardon?"

"That's you. I'm the black sheep; you're the white knight."

"A white night," he said, gesturing with his chin towards the window to underline his pun, "that's once a year if you're lucky, don't you agree? A full moon, starry sky, not a cloud."

Rebeccah smiled at him. There was an attraction, of course, and no sense in denying it, but she already knew enough about him, from family gossip, to know better. She took the edge of her lower lip gently between her teeth and made a decision.

"That's too dizzying an abstraction for this poor lamb," she said, and began to move away.

His hand on her arm brought her up short. "Wait." He looked embarrassed by his abrupt gesture. "I'd like to see you again."

"Again? I'm just going across the room to have a canapé. My stomach is growling. Look over there in a moment and you'll see me."

"I mean," Aaron said, twisting his resolve, "again, after this. Some place else. Perhaps we could have a meal."

"I don't like to cook," Rebeccah said with suspicion.

"I mean in a restaurant," he said in sudden English, as if it were a secret he wanted no one overhearing to understand.

She took a step back and looked him over, from the top of his sandy brown hair, neatly parted in the centre of his well-shaped head, down along the smooth contour of brow, nose, cleanly chiselled mouth and chin, the starched white collar, down the perfectly tied necktie, the immaculate linen jacket, pausing for a moment at his crotch, where, despite the loose drape of his trousers, she believed she saw a barely perceptible movement, then down the crease of the trousers to the glimmering black wings of his oxfords, then up again, letting her eyes take their time while he stood motionless, waiting their verdict. "I want you to know," she said finally, "that you represent just about everything that I detest and abhor about this society, capitalism at its most rapacious, mercantilism at its basest, petty bourgeoisie mentality at its narrowest, dandyism, masculine superiority, class and sexual arrogance..." Her hand darted out from her side in a palm-up gesture of dismay, as if she were overwhelmed by the enormity of the list she was prepared to recite, but her voice trailed off.

Aaron observed her with the same aloof detachment she had spent on him, a small smile seeping into his lips, and he shrugged, a shrug coloured with a boldness that made her think she had, perhaps, been wrong. "I may represent those things," he said. "I think you're wrong, but I won't argue with you now, here. I may *represent* them, but that wouldn't necessarily mean I *am* them. You *are* wrong there."

Four days later, he showed up at the department store where she worked as a window dresser, resplendent in a blue and white striped gabardine suit and a straw hat, a bouquet of flowers in his freshly manicured hand. "We're in the same business," he said as he greeted her with the flow of employees through the staff entrance at six o'clock.

"Not exactly. You sell, I decorate, though I'll concede there's a connection. More importantly, you own, I toil." But she was pleased to see him, flattered by the flowers he now proffered, making a gallant sort of dip with his head and shoulders, his free hand behind his back.

"The same business just the same. Mercantilism at its basest. And the fact that you're a Williams had nothing to do, I suppose, with your getting a job at Loew's."

"I'm not a Williams," Rebeccah said fiercely. "I'm a Kristol."

"Excuse me, no disrespect meant to the memory of your father, who I'm told was a fine man. I regret I never had the pleasure of meeting him. Working here rather than in the family store eases the conscience, don't you agree?"

Rebeccah let a smile slowly form. "That's a contradiction I'm still grappling with, yes." She observed him coolly, conscious of the slight pressure at the back of her neck caused by having to tilt her head upward to meet his eyes. "I don't know that meeting my father would have been a pleasure for you, though. He was a man who said what he thought."

"Like his daughter?"

"Like his daughter, yes."

"There's no accounting for taste," Aaron said, with a light laugh. "Don't you agree?"

He took her to as good a restaurant as was possible, considering the way she was dressed, and afterwards to a place on the lake where they drank wine and danced. He took her home in his automobile, a cream-coloured Packard with shimmering chrome, and, on the street gazed thoughtfully up at the dark windows of her loft, which was on the upper floor of a building that had once been a warehouse and was now honeycombed with small apartments. "You must be lonely there," he said with warmth.

"Not really," Rebeccah answered dryly, considering the options that faced her now. "There are ghosts."

But he didn't ask to come up, didn't make a move to kiss her good night. Instead, he offered his hand and shook hers vigorously.

After that, they saw each other often, dining out, dancing, attending the theatre and concerts, going to the museum and galleries. He had little interest in art, he admitted, and a tin ear, but he seemed happy to accompany her wherever she wished to go, and expressed an interest in learning about the many things for which she had passions. He even, on the two or three occasions when she took him, after the theatre, to a nearby café for coffee and pastries, endured the thinly veiled insults of her friends. Rebeccah made no attempt to defend him and watched thoughtfully as he gingerly fended off Belle's parries, like a man wearing white gloves suddenly handed something slick and foul smelling.

After two months, she was summoned to her Aunt Ruth's for Friday dinner. "And Aaron?" Aunt Ruth inquired after the dishes had been washed and Uncle Avrom had taken the dog and his pipe for a stroll in the late summer evening. The two women sat in the kitchen, drinking cool tea in the flickering candlelight.

"Aaron? That name sounds familiar. Wasn't he a fellow in the Bible?"

"The Bible! You've heard of that, Miss Fancypants, what a surprise."

"My father mentioned it once or twice, said it was suitable for use as kindling, if dead leaves were not close at hand."

"Your father! God rest his soul. He probably did say that. You like him?"

"My father? Of course I liked him." Aunt Ruth had been her mother's closest sister, and Rebeccah had a special affection for her, visiting often since her mother's death. But this was the first time she'd known her to intrude.

"Aaron! Oh, you *know* who I mean. Aaron Greenspun. The man is crazy about you and you don't know who he is."

"Oh, Mr. Goldspun."

"It's Greenspun, dear."

"I know, Aunt Ruth. That's just a little joke."

"A joke! The man wants to marry you and you make jokes about his name that should be your name soon."

Rebeccah stared at her aunt for a moment, then laughed. "Marry me? Aunt Ruth, the man has only kissed me once, and that so softly it felt like a butterfly batting its wings against my lips. And *that* only because it was my birthday. When he escorts me home after an evening together he shakes my hand like it was the handle of a pump and he was dying of thirst."

"The man is a gentleman," Aunt Ruth said sternly. "You don't appreciate that, but you'll learn to."

"The man is beautiful but hollow," Rebeccah retorted. "He's like that candle, flickering, precious, hypnotic if you let yourself look too long, but of no substance." She leaned over and, as if to demonstrate her point, brushed her hand through the small flame, extinguishing it.

"Candles!" Aunt Ruth snorted through her nose. "You're burning yours at both ends, Miss Fancypants. Are you twenty-six now, or is it twenty-seven?"

Rebeccah wrinkled her nose to show her displeasure, but kept her voice soft. "Twenty-five, thank you, just as of three weeks ago, as you well know, since you sent me that lovely crinoline robe." She paused, tilting her chin up slightly. "You *witch*. I thought that was an odd gift to be coming from you. You're preparing my trousseau, aren't you?"

"Your mother, God rest her soul, isn't here to look after you. You're incapable of doing it yourself, so someone has to. It's a burden, but I take it happily, *Bubala*."

The two women stared at each other through the growing darkness that had pounced on the room when the candle went out. Finally, Rebeccah blinked. "What do you mean, he wants to marry me?"

"Just that. Would it be plainer if I spoke in English?"

"You're crazy, Aunt Ruth. Forgive me for saying so. How do you dream of such things?"

"There's no dreaming, Miss Fancypants. The man said so himself."

"Said so. To whom? You?"

"Not to me, of course, silly," Aunt Ruth said. "To Uncle Meyer. He was a bit flummoxed, the poor man, his nose always in the store's books, he hardly knows there's a real world spinning around him, he asked me to have a word with you, and your Uncle Avrom to look after things. Oh, for goodness sake, Rebeccah, sit back down."

Rebeccah was on her feet, her hands closing into small, tight fists at her side. "He told Uncle Meyer he wanted to marry me? Aaron Greenspun did that?"

"Of course he did, *Bubala*. Now sit down."

She was speechless, words spinning around in her mind but failing properly to lodge on her tongue, like gears in a machine that won't engage. Worse, she felt, inexplicably, a profound sense of shame, as if she had been caught out in some disgusting betrayal, and blood rushed to her cheeks, making her feel faint. "Who...who..." she stammered.

"Who does he think he is? A gentleman, that's who." Aunt Ruth put her hand on Rebeccah's wrist and tugged at it until she sat down. "Let me ask you this, Miss Modern Woman, Miss Artist and Literary Type. If your father, God rest his soul, were alive, and if Aaron Greenspun or any other man, I mean any other man of breeding and manners, this isn't your friends like Morgenstern or that actor I'm talking about, but men who still have the old country in their minds and hearts, if such a man wanted to marry you and your father was alive, wouldn't you expect such a man to have the courtesy of talking to your father. *Not*" – she held up a silencing hand – "to ask permission, just to inform. Wouldn't you expect that? Wouldn't you even, maybe, be hurt, just a little, if such a man didn't do that, Miss Head-in-the-Clouds?"

Rebeccah allowed that maybe she would, "if it was

Dave Margoshes

that type of man, yes, maybe. Not if Morgenstern didn't do it." And she laughed at that thought, of my father paying a courtesy call.

"Well, what an admission! But Mr. Greenspun *is* that sort of man. He's a gentleman and an old country man. And wait, wait just a second, darling, let me ask you one more thing. Since your father, God rest his soul, *isn't* here, wouldn't it be proper then for Mr. Greenspun to talk to some other member of the Kristol family, if there was one nearby? Your father's brother, Mort, maybe, except that he lives a thousand miles away?"

Rebeccah nodded slowly.

"So, all right. Your father, God rest his soul, isn't alive, nor, God rest her soul, is your mother, my darling Rebeccah, and your father's brother and other relatives are a thousand miles away. So whom should Mr. Greenspun talk to about his intentions but your Uncle Meyer. Woolly headed though he is, he *is* the head of the Williams family, your mother's people."

"He could have talked to *me*, damn it," Rebeccah said in English.

Aunt Ruth smiled and patted Rebeccah's hand, which had grown cold. "He will, *Bubala*, he will. As soon as I tell him you'd like him to. Oh, come on, come on. He's a gentleman, I keep telling you. And maybe just a little bit shy, too."

Rebeccah went home and, over the next three days, as she brushed her teeth and combed her hair, as she steamed her vegetables for dinner, as she painted, standing nude under the skylights of her loft, she contemplated her life. She was, in fact, twenty-five years old, and, as her father had died at sixty-eight, her mother at sixty-three, she was well into what was likely the second third of her life. There had been no money left after her mother's illness, so her father's wispy promises that maybe, someday, she would go to art school had entirely evaporated. She had delayed her departure to New York and points further on so long that, now, the thought of leaving Cleveland terrified her. And, worse yet, the paintings she had done, piled up like neatly stacked picket signs waiting the next strike in her father's old office at the union hall, even the painting she was working on now, were shit, no other word for it, in Yiddish, English or any other language. She sighed, lit another cigarette and went to stand in front of her one concession to vanity, a full-length mirror she had justified when she bought it as essential to her study of anatomy. She stood there, in the bright, white northern light streaming down from the ceiling window, for a long time, observing the beginning sag of her breasts, the little puckering of skin along her belly.

On the third day, Monday, when Aaron came to call for her at the store, she found herself looking at him more closely than usual, *examining* him, with her painter's eye, as if looking for defects to match the ones she had found in herself. He had shaven within the hour and there were tiny pinpricks of dried blood clustered along the firm line of his jaw, but his cheeks and neck, when she reached across the table suddenly to stroke them, taking him aback and bringing a pleased, bashful smile to his strong mouth, were smooth as a baby's. His yellow eyes glistened like those of a cat watching the progress of a mouse across the room, and she had to admit he was simply beautiful, as flawless as a baby that had not yet begun to puncture its possibilities. But, at the same time, he was hollow, as she had told her aunt, filled with vapid observations about the weather, the people who worked for him in his shop, the politics of the city. Two weeks before, she remembered, after the theatre, an Ibsen play, his only comment had been a vague "What a way to live."

"You don't have an idea in your head, do you?" she asked suddenly, surprising herself that the thought had translated itself into words, slipping out of her mouth before she could stop them. Aaron blinked, looked surprised but not particularly displeased, as if her comment had referred to his new jacket, a grey seersucker he had taken off the rack that afternoon.

"I have an idea that I'd like to get to know you better. How's that?"

Rebeccah smiled despite herself. So it was out, the overture that, from almost any other man of her acquaintance, likely would have come on the first night, certainly on the second, but from Aaron Greenspun had taken two months. She wondered if he had spoken with her aunt over the weekend, whether something she had said had emboldened him. Well, it didn't matter. The next step was up to her.

"That would be very nice," she said. "Yes, I'd like that."

That was all there was to it. So simple, that small exchange, but now there was an understanding between them, and that night, for the first time, when he had escorted her home, he kissed her good night, and she knew the inexorable journey to their marriage had begun.

The engagement was announced within weeks but the marriage itself didn't take place until the following spring, after a suitable period of adjustment to the idea and an opportunity for Aaron to purchase and, with Rebeccah's guidance, furnish a house, in the growing suburb of Shaker Heights, where streets lay like quiet ribbons beneath tall canopies of leaves. The honeymoon was to include an overnight trip on a paddlewheel schooner that plied Lake Erie, taking them from Cleveland to Buffalo, from where they would go by train to Niagara Falls, there spending several days admiring the scenery. It would be aboard the ship, on its first night out, in their stateroom, that their marriage was to be consummated. It was not a fit topic for conversation between betrothed, but Aaron, always a gentleman, did have this observation to make, three weeks before the wedding, when Rebeccah was still assembling the items for her trousseau: "And as to the rest...what will come afterwards...well, I just want you to have no concern. I'm not entirely without experience" – here he offered her his shyest smile, while his eyes blazed with boldness – "and I can promise you that I'll be gentle. It will be something wonderful, the two of us, don't you agree?"

Rebeccah awaited that something wonderful with a great deal of concern, in fact, since she was not without some *considerable* experience herself. The subject of virginity was not discussed, but it became clear to her, both from Aaron's manner and occasional small things he said, that he assumed he would be the first man to share sex with her – although he knew she had many male friends, most of whom he disapproved of – and that it was important to him. Honesty seemed out of the question, and the strategy of deception appeared to be inevitable.

"That will be no trouble at all. Don't worry your head about it," her friend Belle told her. She was a woman of indeterminable age but at least beyond forty to judge from the wealth of experience she had crammed into her life, a Romanian who had travelled for several years in France and England on her way to America, a friend, so she said, of Virginia Woolf and

Emma Goldman, a painter of note who had benefited Rebeccah with encouragement and gentle criticism, a lesbian, though that was not a term then in vogue, who had buried three husbands already, one in each of the previous countries where she'd lived. "Men are such children, it's easy to deceive them. Flatter them and they're only too happy to believe anything, no matter how unlikely." She puffed on one of the slim black cigars she had developed a taste for in Paris and raised her magnificent eyebrows. "When it comes to sex, it's all the easier since, in bed, they are so helpless. So *strong*, they think they are, just because blood rushes to one pathetic portion of their anatomy and makes it stiff. At the same time, the rest of them turns to jelly." She shrugged her shoulders and gestured with a slim, black-gloved hand, as if uncovering some vast expanse. "Men are such children, take it from me, darling Rebeccah. They preen and swagger, they bellow and fight, they spend money like it was water and let compliments flow from their tongues like honey from the rock, they even *marry* you, so desperate are some of them, all to get you in bed, then a little kiss, a little pat, a jiggle, a thrust, another jiggle and it's all over. They roll over and lie there like exhausted warriors who have single-handedly defeated great armies, a beatific smile playing about their lips like a butterfly among flowers. No, don't worry your head, darling, it will be easy to deceive your Mr. Spun-From-Gold. We'll devise a plan."

The deception was remarkably simple, consisting of an easily mixed douche of water, vinegar and alum, guaranteed, Belle promised, to give Rebeccah the rasping friction of a thirteen-year-old girl, and a small quantity of chicken blood, concealed in a pink balloon, the sort that children blow up at birthday parties. The rest, Belle explained, was merely a sleight of hand, a bit of acting and, she said, "that famous guile we women are supposed to have in such abundance. Let's see if it's true." And, on the couch in Belle's studio, not far from Rebeccah's own loft, they practiced the weary motions, with Belle taking Aaron's part.

"Ah, my darling, my sweet *cheri*, don't be frightened, I weeell be gentle," she sing-songed in English rich with French resonance, and the two of them burst into schoolgirl giggles, rolling together on the sofa like young athletes, though it went no further than that. "Ah, my darling," Belle gasped, breathless with laughter, "you are so, how they say? Wonderfully...tight."

Rebeccah herself went to the pharmacist for the alum, and prepared the mixture as to Belle's instructions, starting its use two days before the wedding, to be sure. "I feel like the inside of a pickled egg," she reported.

"Ah, how wonderfully tasty," Belle retorted, arching her brows.

But Belle, on the day of the wedding itself, so it would be fresh, attended to the blood, visiting at the slaughterhouse a *kosher* rabbi she was acquainted with, who provided what she needed, no questions asked.

The wedding was small, by the standards of the community, with only family, from Akron as well as Cleveland, and a few of Rebeccah's and Aaron's closest friends attending. Rebeccah had doubted most of her café friends would be interested, or would approve; besides, she had found herself, in recent months, drifting away from them, with the exception of Belle and a couple of other women. Uncle Meyer, as head of the family, and the wealthiest, hosted the party at his home in the Heights, though Uncle Avrom, as the favourite uncle, played the part of the surrogate father, standing up to give the bride away. Aaron broke the muffled glass with one determined stomp, there was dizzying music, crowded tables of food that all seemed to be flavoured with honey and glasses of sweet wine that couldn't be emptied. Then, as her head spun, Rebeccah was led by the hand to a waiting motorcar by Aaron, her husband – *her husband* – and they were off to the docks.

Her head was still filled with spinning wafts of wool when they were shown to their cabin, and as soon as the porter was gone, Aaron had her in his arms, covering her mouth, nose, ears and neck with moist, indistinct kisses. She extricated herself, took her overnight bag and locked herself in the small bathroom where she made one final application of the douche before putting on her nightgown. Then, with the balloon cupped in her palm, she made her entrance.

"You look wonderful, darling," Aaron said in English, his yellow eyes seeming to dance in the soft glow of the kerosene lamp. "You get into bed. I'll just be a minute."

She did as he said and, as soon as the door softly shut behind him, slipped the balloon under her pillow. Then, with her eyes gradually slipping into a sharp focus on what was either a stain or a shadow on the ceiling, she waited, her breath ragged, her heart pounding, just as if she really were a virgin.

Afterwards, as Aaron slept, Rebeccah put a robe over her gown, slid her feet into slippers and crept from the cabin to walk along the deserted deck. The night was thick and dark, like an old woollen cloak, and cold. She stood against the rail, shivering and clutching her arms, staring down at where, from the choppy roll of the deck beneath her feet, she could tell the foaming waves of the lake were splattering against the ship's hull. But she could see nothing and even the sound of the waves was absent, drowned out by the whining of the engines, which must have been close by where she stood. She could have just as easily been aboard one of Jules Verne's fantastic ships, sailing through the darkness of space, as on the paddlewheeler *Albany*, somewhere in the middle of Lake Erie, suspended between two countries and two worlds. The deception had been so simple, so absurdly successful, just as Belle had promised. Aaron had been still a little drunk, his shining eyes excited but only half open as he slipped into bed and turned to her, and he'd been hasty, clumsy, needing, despite her pretense of innocence, her discreet hand to guide him. The alum had done its job almost too well, and there'd been pain, for him as well as her, and then it was over, almost before it had begun, leaving her barely enough time to reach back beneath the pillow for the balloon, sliding it down along her sweaty side, before he rolled away. She clenched it tightly in her palm, pricking it with the nail of her index finger, and smeared the tepid blood along her thighs and into the dripping wet hair covering her aching vulva. She had lain there for a moment, feeling like the victim of some bizarre religious ritual, waiting for him to lift the sheet, seeking the evidence for himself, but as it happened he was already drifting off to sleep, one hand tossed lightly across her breast like a statement of trust and possession, and he never did look.

Just before he screwed his face closer into the pillow and fell asleep, as quickly and firmly as a stone being dropped into water, he half opened his eyes and murmured: "That was wonderful, darling, don't you agree?"

She hadn't said anything, just watched, in the flickering light of the lamp, as he fell asleep. She'd insisted he leave the lamp burning, so she could see him, those brilliant cat's eyes, so he could see her, because he was so beautiful and she wanted to feel beautiful. But after they started, he had closed his eyes, and it had seemed to her he could have been anyone. Just the same, there had been a moment, as he slid into her, a moment above the pain as her nerve endings and skin responded on their own, when they had moved together as one, when her passion had risen with the alacrity all those months of courtship seemed to have been foreshadowing and their breaths had merged into one fierce, staccato rhythm. She thought about that moment as she stood along the railing, her teeth chattering with cold, her eyes streaming with tears as they stared blankly into the darkness below. There had been that moment, that was all. There had even been one moment when, allowing her imagination to run wild, she had believed she might love him. But it had just been that one moment, and then it was gone.

A Romantic Secret

A few years after his return to New York from out west, but before the introduction to my mother that would change his life, my father met and became friendly with a man to whom he would always refer, usually accompanied by a wink, as "the notorious Leon Arrow."

Years later, when I was a teenager, I met this Arrow myself, but whatever appeal he had had for my father was lost on me. My father's stories of his friend's past – notorious indeed – and the reality of the man I met were so much in conflict that I was immediately confused.

At that time, he was working as a middle-level functionary in the Bronx offices of the Plumbers, Pipefitters and Joiners Union, a job more involved with bookkeeping and paper shuffling than organizing or negotiating. To me, it seemed a fairly humdrum occupation, totally lacking in any of the drama or glamour I knew – from reading Steinbeck and Dos Passos and from hearing my father's tales of the old days – some work in the labour movement possessed. Moreover, he was a nondescript, dishevelled man inhabiting what was to me still the mysterious upper middle ages of life: short, slump-shouldered, pot-bellied and lame, a combination that produced a slightly comical imbalance in his posture and walk; balding, with a rim of mouse-coloured hair above his ears and running behind his skull, as if he were wearing ill-fitting earmuffs; and wearing wire-rimmed glasses that failed to conceal the hangdog, always moist brown eyes behind them. He looked, in short, like a lot of the men who were my father's friends or colleagues, whom I would sometimes meet on the rare occasions when I visited him at the newspaper office, and who to me – twelve and thirteen and fourteen at the time – were of very little interest. Notorious? My father's adjective seemed misplaced.

But I did have some interest in this Arrow, not because of his appearance or occupation but because of what my father had told me of his past. He was a reformed Communist who had renounced not only his former beliefs but his former comrades and so lived in a sort of social netherworld, distrusted by both his former friends and his new colleagues, not really liked by anyone, with the exception of my father, who, though wary, was loyal to a fault. He was a husband and father long separated from his family, having left them somewhere in the Midwest – Minnesota, my father thought – to pursue single-mindedly his political goals. And now, those goals unrealized, the beliefs that fuelled them turned to ashes, he found himself alone, guilty and bereft. He had been injured – the cause of his limp – and arrested in the improbably named city of Winnipeg somewhere in the heart of Canada, during a brawl that climaxed what my father described to me as the infamous General Strike of 1919, when the flooding of the job market by thousands of returning soldiers further inflamed the labour movement of that backwater city, and he had spent several years in a Canadian prison before being deported. And he'd served another term in prison later on for a crime about which my father was vague. But even more fascinating than all that to me was this: he was a man, my father had told me, "with a romantic secret." What that secret was, my father wouldn't say.

"He is a man with a colourful past, that's for sure," my father said, somewhat enigmatically.

"Romantic secret" – what a powerful phrase that was for me at my impressionable age. I too had romantic secrets, but they were, I knew, trivial, even on their own and certainly in comparison to those of a man who had been beaten, jailed, his life turned inside out. So I was curious to meet Leon Arrow and, one summer afternoon when, at my father's invitation, I had taken the subway into Manhattan to have lunch with him, and he told me his notorious friend would be joining us, I was pleased.

But when I actually met the man, as I said, my interest quickly cooled. I already knew that his job was a far cry from the activities of his swashbuckling past, but this was true of a number of my father's friends, as it was even of my father himself: he once had aspirations to be a novelist and poet, but he made his living as a reporter covering the labour beat for a Yiddish newspaper. "Life is compromise," he was fond of saying. "Things don't work out as you plan. And," he would add with a wink, "sometimes that's just as well."

With that in mind, even at thirteen or fourteen, I could see Arrow's present lot in life as a price he was paying for the excesses of his youth. If anything, that made him even more fascinating to me. But Leon Arrow's physical appearance was in such contrast to the romantic figure I had imagined – someone drawn and haunted but ruggedly handsome, like Humphrey Bogart, say, or Ronald Coleman – that I couldn't help but avert my eyes, and I bit my tongue to keep from laughing out loud at the cruel irony of his name, *Arrow*, implying something straight and true and sharp. My father saw this, and perhaps Arrow did as well; at any rate, the conversation between the two men, which so far had been limited to welcoming pleasantries, soon shifted to Yiddish, deliberately excluding me. I ate my tuna salad sandwich and cherry Jell-O – we were at the Automat on Pearl Street, not too far from my father's office and one of his regular haunts – and took my leave after a decent interval. "Nice to have met you, young man," Arrow said as he shook my hand. His grip was firm and he looked me in the eye with a frank, unblinking gaze, as if he were seeing beyond my skin, appraising the inner me, the real me, as if in rebuke for my failure to afford him the same courtesy. Behind his smudged spectacles, his softened brown eyes, the colour of coffee as my father drank it, with a good splash of milk, seemed lively and intelligent. On the subway back to Brooklyn, I couldn't help feeling that I had somehow missed an opportunity.

"Don't judge books by their covers," my father said that evening, referring to the lunch. He didn't say it sharply.

It wasn't till I was grown that my father told me more about his friend, revealing his secret.

Leon Arrow arrived in New York some time in 1927, my father said, through a circuitous route, and with three marriages already behind him. There would be at least one more.

He was an organizer for the Communist party, active in the plumbers' union – which was then overrun with Communists, my father explained – and a veteran of the Wobblies, the legendary One Big Union. "There was a hint," my father said, "that he was not just an organizer for the Communists, but a Soviet agent of some sort. These people were secretive, so it was hard to tell."

My father had no problem with Communists in those days – indeed, he would marry a woman whose father was active in the party and had taken part in Bolshevik activities in Russia. It was only later, after the Communist-led strike at my father's newspaper, *The Day*, that he soured on the party, which he felt had beguiled and betrayed the strikers.

The two men first met at the Café Royale, a Lower East Side hangout for intellectuals and artists on Second Avenue that my father frequented. My father was neither a true artist nor an intellectual, by his own admission, but had inclinations in that direction and was interested in such people and the hangers-on who flocked around them, among whom he cheerfully classified himself. Leon Arrow was also such a hanger-on, for reasons of his own that weren't apparent, since few if any members of the plumbers' union spent time there, though leaders of the various garment workers' unions did, and labour ferment and strategy was often a topic of conversation at the Royale's tables. The two men took a liking to each other and, under the influence of *schnapps* at a nearby saloon, Arrow's tongue became looser than it should have been.

"Three marriages – and no divorces?" my father said with surprise after hearing the other man's revelation.

"No," Arrow admitted ruefully. "It wasn't deliberate, Morgenstern. These things happen."

Arrow, my father learned, was the son of a Minneapolis hardware wholesaler who had modified the family name from Aronofsky. He'd fallen out with his family ("bourgeois shits," he called them) while still in his teens and found a job, through a friend of a friend, as a plumber's assistant. He was, by his own admission, foolish in love and married a girl entirely unsuited to him, although, my father told me, "it would be hard to say what type of woman *would* have been suited to him, he was so sour a man." But my father admitted he didn't know Arrow in his youth, and he might then have been of a more positive frame of mind. The man's time in prison had a profound effect on him, my father believed. "When I met him," my father said, "he was an entirely unlovable man. He could be likeable, though. That's what drew me to him, obviously."

With this first wife, Arrow had two children, in rapid, unthinking succession. She was a woman who might well have fit in with his family, and although love was soon gone he was a conscientious if not devoted husband and father. He was a conscientious worker as well, and it was within reason to believe that he would have his plumber's journeyman ticket soon, and some-day, perhaps, be in business for himself. Then, already leaning to the left, the result of passionate tavern con-versations with other young tradesmen, he was caught up in the deeper passion of the One Big Union move-ment as it swept across the American heartland. It was this that led him, along with several friends, across the border into Canada when they heard talk of the general strike fomenting in Winnipeg. They wanted to be part of it, to see if there were lessons that might be applied to Minneapolis.

With some of his fellows, Arrow, who had an impetu-ous nature, was swept up in the excitement of the strike, and on Black Sunday, when the Mounted Police charged the marchers, he joined in the group of hot-heads who set a streetcar on its side. As it toppled, Arrow slipped and fell, and felt a piece of metal, an ornament on the exterior of the streetcar but with all the weight of the streetcar behind it, brush against his ankle – "just a kiss," he told my father, "but enough to break the bone." He was arrested with a stout stick in his hand as he attempted to hobble away – a policeman testified at his trial that Arrow brandished the stick as a weapon. His American citizenship was further held against him and he was sentenced to three years at Stony Mountain Prison for violations of the Riot Act. During his time there, he did much to keep the water in the old jail's rusty pipes flowing, and he was released after only two years, and summarily deported.

All during his absence he heard nothing from his family in Minneapolis, neither his parents and siblings – whom he didn't try to contact but must surely have known of his plight – nor his wife, to whom he dutifully wrote several times. No reply. His feelings of love for his wife had long since been extinguished, and now his sense of responsibility towards her and the children, a boy and girl who, at this point, would have been five and four, and whom, he realized, he barely knew, was seriously weakened, thin as a thread about to snap. As a result, on his release, Arrow felt little compunction about ignoring his obligations to them, he told my father. "Fuck them," he said with a casual shrug of his shoulders. Still, had he been deported to Minneapolis, he might well have tried to find them, but for some reason he was sent instead to Detroit, where he succumbed to the easier path, finding work at one of the numerous parts plants that catered to the automobile industry, making hoses and fittings.

He was only twenty-five, a healthy young man, lonely and hungry for companionship and sex, and was soon enmeshed in a romance with a waitress at the café where he occasionally took a meal. She was "a nobody, a nothing," he told my father with a dismissive wave of his hand. Nonetheless, things followed their natural course and "hardly before I knew it, we were married," he said. A divorce from the first wife was merely overlooked, not ignored, "an oversight," Arrow said. "I had every intention...then I was overtaken by events."

History soon repeated itself. In prison, Arrow had met some Communists and become attracted to their ideas. In Detroit, he joined the party and became increasingly active. Love cooled between him and his new wife, and when the party sent him on a mission to Pittsburgh, Pennsylvania, he left her behind, without any clear plan in mind, though he suspected she was just as glad to see the back of him. In Pittsburgh, there was another woman, this time a dancer at a nightclub with, he told my father, "looser morals than I was used to." He was swept away and, when she became pregnant, they married. Again, divorce from the woman he was no longer in contact with was overlooked.

"If you think I am a criminal in this matter, think again," Arrow insisted. "I'm a victim of circumstances."

"Circumstances largely of your own making," my father replied.

"Well, all right then. Of stupidity, I plead guilty. But criminal intent, no."

"And the dancer?" my father asked.

"I told you, her morals were loose. No, I'm being generous – she had *no* morals. She was a tramp, but she fancied herself an *artiste*. She didn't even care if we married. It was I who insisted, for the sake of the child. She couldn't care less if I was divorced or not."

So when the party sent him to New York, he went with pleasure, glad to shake the dust of the Midwest, which he pronounced "a shithole, one big shithole filled with smaller shitholes," from his feet. The latest wife and child were also left behind, with no ceremony. By this point in Arrow's recounting of his life, my father had developed some distaste for the man, as it appeared to him that it was Arrow who had exhibited the loose morals, not the dancer, but he was intrigued enough by him and his story that he was willing to hold his nose.

Arrow was then about thirty, still in good health, still lonely, still hungry. He was short but, as my father described him, good looking, fit and athletic, despite his limp, with a full head of dark wavy hair, usually Brylcreemed back, and penetrating brown eyes that women, apparently, found especially attractive. He always had a suspiciously large amount of money in his pocket for drinks and meals, and he often treated the artists he fell into conversation with at the Café Royale. He dressed well too, certainly better than any plumber or other tradesman my father had ever known. "If a woman saw him walking down the street, she might well think 'there goes a good catch'," my father said. Indeed, his limp, which was not so bad as to be repellant or make him an object of pity, suggested some dangerous living in his past, and made him even more attractive to women, my father believed. "Women like a suggestion of weakness in a strong man," my father said, with a wink.

Had a woman whose eye was caught by Arrow drawn closer, though, she might well change her mind, my father thought. The man had so dark a view of life, so sour a disposition, it was hard for my father to imagine any woman wanting to spend much time with him. Unlike most Communists and other left-wingers of my father's acquaintance, who believed in a better life, or the Revolution or some other brighter tomorrow, Leon Arrow was thoroughly cynical, believing the worst of most people – with Marx, Lenin and Stalin notable exceptions – and situations. His adventure in Winnipeg and his time in prison, where he claimed to have witnessed unspeakable behaviours, on the part of both inmates and their guards, had certainly soured him.

"The revolution will come," he would pronounce, "not because we make it come, want it to come, will it to come, but because it will on its own. It's inevitable. A proper reading of Marx makes that clear. To struggle against it is unthinkable. To work for it is merely to hasten the day of its certain arrival, and to be on the side of the angels, such as they are. But to think that life will be automatically better, well, that would be naive, even foolish. Life will be what it will be. If we struggle to make it better, it might be."

Even the leadership of the Communist Party – sacrosanct for most members – was cast in a cynical light. "You think that when we are in charge, we will be better, more humane, more reasonable?" Arrow would ask rhetorically. "Why would you think that? The system will be better, of course, so our leadership will *seem* better. Beyond that, who can say? Our leaders are certainly better men than the leaders of the capitalists and reactionaries, but they are only men, not gods or even saints. Mistakes? We all make plenty, and so do they. As for myself, I can only say that I am a man like any other. I don't think anyone else can claim more."

This position was so in contrast to what one normally heard about the party from its adherents that my father couldn't help but wonder if it wasn't a pose, something to make Arrow more approachable to those who feared or distrusted Communists and communism. "But later," my father said, "when he left the party, when he became embittered – well, *more* bitter, I should say – when he became a vocal anti-communist, there wasn't really all that much of a change in what he had to say. He changed his stripes but underneath he was the same tiger."

Arrow's cynicism extended to his personal views as well as his political ones. Although he was usually discreet about his own experiences with marriage, he was critical of marriage as an institution, was dismissive of children, sarcastic about romance.

And though he was certainly still attracted to women, my father said, he was generally dismissive of them. Often, referring to a woman he knew or even a strange woman passing by on the street, he would use the offensive terms "slut" or "whore" or the Yiddish *kurveh* and *nafkeh*, which translate to much the same.

"Women are the capitalists of the domestic world," my father heard him proclaim on several occasions. "Men do all the labour, women reap the rewards. Children, once they pass the age of pure innocence, are the complicit middle class. Is the wife really so different from the boss?"

This would invariably provoke a predictable response from the fellows who shared a table with him: "I'm the boss in my family," one or several of them would loudly insist.

"So you may think," Arrow would reply, aiming a wink at whoever he thought was most sympathetic to his view. "In many factories and mines and on the railroads, the unions believe they call the tune. They can halt work with a whistle from the steward. But who is on the best terms with their bankers, would you say – the workers or the owners?"

Again, this would produce a predictable response. "That may all be true on the shop floor, Arrow," someone would protest, "but in my household, I am the boss, believe me."

"So you may think, so you may think," Arrow would say, and again that condescending wink.

"There really wasn't anything about him a woman would find appealing," my father said, "except, maybe, the challenge."

That must have been it, because, according to my father, women seemed to find him irresistible. At the Café Royale, there were always women around him, hanging on his every sour word, and he seemed never to be at loss for female company for the theatre, dinner or union dances.

My father recounted an incident he recalled vividly: "We were seated at a table, Arrow, myself and several others, including a woman named Lily Siegel, a poet. The name of another woman was mentioned and Arrow sneered, 'that one's just a cunt surrounded by a body.' Excuse my language. Lily winced but she said nothing, just kept smiling. It was left to me to object." He shook his head.

"Some women have a weakness for such things," my father said with a perplexed sigh and a wink to me. "They're all do-gooders, you know, women." Comments like that were usually said outside of the hearing of my mother. She would be in the living room, reading or listening to music. My father would be sitting at the kitchen table in his undershirt, drinking port from a water glass. "They think they can save lost men, reform bad ones." He gazed into his glass, then took a sip. "But some men can't be saved."

One of the women attracted to Leon Arrow, my father noticed, seemed to have a proprietary interest in him, taking his arm as they walked, sugaring and stirring his coffee for him. She was a tall, nicely dressed woman, a looker, with bobbed honey-coloured hair often partly covered by fashionable hats. Her name was Henrietta Himmelfarb and she worked, my father learned, as a designer for the garment company her father owned.

He also learned, early one mid-winter week, that she and Arrow had abruptly gotten married on the weekend, having taken the overnight train to Maryland, where there was no waiting period, then back before Monday morning.

"I was carried away," Arrow confessed to my father, with just a touch of sheepishness to his usually brash tone. "Swept off my feet."

"Aren't you taking a chance, though?" my father asked.

"What do you mean?"

"Well, your other marriages..."

"Oh, that," Arrow said dismissively, as if that matter of inconvenience had entirely slipped his mind but was nevertheless of little consequence. "What Henrietta doesn't know won't hurt her." He gave my father a penetrating look, as if daring him to reveal the secret. "Nor anyone else."

The newlyweds took up housekeeping in an apartment on West Seventy-Eighth Street, a long subway ride from the Café Royale and the Lower East Side where Henrietta worked and Leon Arrow carried out his mysterious comings, goings and discussions. Soon, it became known that the new Mrs. Arrow was pregnant, and had left her job, and that her disapproving family had cut her off. Since money was never an issue for her husband, that should not have been a problem, but apparently it was, my father said. "Somehow, he had overextended himself." The rumour was that the party was as displeased with Arrow's behaviour as the bride's family was with hers and had pulled his leash tight.

For the first few weeks of this arrangement, my father continued to run into Arrow occasionally on East Broadway and at the Café Royale on evenings, both men bundled up in overcoats, scarves and hats against the unusual February cold, and after this had happened two or three times, my father jokingly greeted him, "That wife of yours has kicked you out already, Arrow? And in this weather?" to which his friend first blanched, then reddened. "That's no concern of yours, Morgenstern," he said sharply.

My father, chastened, began to apologize but Arrow waved it off and they turned to other conversation as if nothing had happened. But a few days later, my father became aware that he hadn't seen Arrow for a while, and, thinking back, realized it hadn't been since the day of that exchange. Several more days followed without Arrow making an appearance at the café. When he did return, it was in the form of a changed man, subdued, pale, shaky. He actually seemed smaller, my father said. His limp seemed more pronounced.

"Arrow, what is it?" my father inquired.

They sat down at a table and ordered coffees. Arrow's eyes were red, as if he had been many hours without sleep or even had been crying, although that seemed so unlikely my father shook the idea away.

"Henrietta..." he began, faltering. "There was an accident..."

"Is she all right?" my father asked.

"She's...she's dead."

"Good Lord, man, what happened?"

"An accident," Arrow repeated, but gradually, in fragments, my father got the story out of him, or some semblance of it: Arrow had taken her for an abortion, and she'd seemed fine afterwards, but soon after they returned to their apartment she'd begun to hemorrhage. He'd hesitated in taking her to the hospital and then, when he did, the two of them drenched in her blood, it was too late. She died in the taxicab on the way.

"My God," my father said.

When he looked up, my father told me, Arrow's face was ashen and fat seemed to have drained from his cheeks, so pinched were they.

Things went very badly for Leon Arrow after that, my father said. The hospital, of course, had reported the incident of Henrietta's death to the police and Arrow was soon brought in for questioning. From that point, the situation spiralled downward quickly. A warrant for his arrest from Minneapolis was discovered – it seemed that his first wife had pursued him through the courts for child support and somehow news had surfaced of the second marriage in Detroit, where child support had also been ordered; payments for both were long overdue, and he had been found in contempt of court *in absentia*. He wound up serving two consecutive prison terms, one in New York for bigamy and his involvement with the abortion, and somewhere in the Midwest for the contempt and another bigamy charge, seven years in all. It could have been even worse had the marriage to the dancer in Pittsburgh ever come to light.

When Arrow came out of prison, he drifted back to New York and eventually found work with the plumbers' union, where he still had contacts, though, by this time, it had long since purged itself of most of its known Communists. But he was a broken man in many ways, my father said, and his bitterness could make him unpleasant company. They saw each other infrequently – that lunch at the Automat when I'd met him and been so unimpressed was one of those rare occasions – and my father said Arrow never spoke of his personal life so he didn't know if he had married again, if there had been any more women.

My father had testified as a character witness at Arrow's trial in New York. He pleaded not guilty, of course, claiming he was a victim of circumstances. The bigamy, he testified and his lawyer argued, was no more than an oversight, certainly not a criminal act. As to the abortion, he swore he knew his wife was undergoing a medical procedure at the clinic he brought her to, but no more, and his lawyer argued passionately that Arrow had been punished enough by Henrietta's death. My father, somewhat reluctantly, testified that Arrow was a good person, concerned with his fellow man, and that he'd never heard him boast of any wrongdoing. This was true enough, but when he was cross-examined, my father had to admit he was aware of Arrow's previous marriages, that he spoke openly of them.

All of this would weigh heavily on my father a couple of years later when he met the woman who would be my mother and started to think seriously of marriage himself. It was an institution cloaked in ritual and mystery, with its vows of love, honour and obedience, and Arrow, it seemed to my father, had violated every tenet of those vows, and with barely a thought or a regret. Yet he was not a bad fellow, not really. He hadn't entered into his marriages as a sexual predator or with the intention of bilking the women of their savings or from any other ulterior motive. He had been, he'd confessed at his trial, "careless," and that was the word that stayed with my father.

It gave my father pause to think that it might be possible to distort so easily the very best of intentions.

✿ ✿ ✿

A Distant Relation

The same year, late in the last century, that my grandfather left his wife and children to cross the ocean to New York, where it was thought he might make a better life, his older brother, whose name was Isaac, left his family as well and went, with a similar purpose, to Montreal.

The two brothers had never been close. As children, only two among many brothers and sisters on a farm, they had been rivals for their often absent father's attention, and as adults they had little in common – Joseph, my grandfather, a newspaper writer and editor, an intellectual of sorts, Isaac a brawler and a fixer, good with his hands. This characterization, apparently, was the extent of what my grandfather had to say about his brother. In their new countries, they did not have any direct contact, but, through other relatives, they heard news of each other, and, consequently, my father was dimly, disinterestedly, aware that he had an uncle and aunt, and a brood of cousins, in Canada. Why one brother had come to one North American country while the other went to the other, my father didn't know – perhaps their destinations had merely been an accident. All he did know, in fact, was that he had relatives in Montreal, a city that, while it was considerably closer, seemed as distant and exotic as the cities of Poland and Russia that figured in *his* father's recollections. In his own travels, north into upstate New York and New Hampshire, and west into Ohio and Illinois, my father never gave these relatives a thought.

So when, early in 1930, he met his cousin Reuben one evening in the crowded Automat on Pearl Street, he was flabbergasted. They were first cousins, sons of brothers, with a noticeable similarity in the shape of their faces and features, but the distance between them was more than one merely to be measured in miles or the texture of blood.

My father, who was a reporter at *The Day*, was with Vogel, his counterpart at *The Forward*, the Socialist paper. Together, the two men, rivals but friends, kept their eyes on the city's teeming garment district and its boisterous, muscular unions. On this night, they were eating together because, within the hour, they were due at a meeting of Local 37, the cutters, who were agitating for a strike within the industry – the merits of which my father, who was opposed, and Vogel, who was enthusiastically in support, were arguing. And they were at the Automat because the union meeting hall they'd soon be heading towards was nearby.

My father was eating hotdogs and beans, for which he had deposited three nickels into the slots beside the glass window, one of dozens of such windows in the wall separating the dining area from the kitchen. On his tray was a cup of almost white coffee, from which he sipped as he ate, and a bowl of red Jell-O with a crown of whipped cream; both of these had cost a nickel extra. He had squeezed bright yellow mustard over his plate and was eating with gusto, aiding his fork with a crust of bread.

Vogel, who rarely ate, was slurping from a cup of black coffee and chain-smoking cigarettes. He was a small man, little larger than a child, with a narrow skull, and already had the same nervous mannerisms which, years later, when I came to know him, were always so noticeable: a twitch in his eyelid, an irritation in his ear that made him continuously tap at the base of his jaw with his fingertips. Both men were in their thirties, my father a year or two older than his friend, unmarried, dressed in dark suits and ties, in good health, their hair still thick and dark, though my father's was beginning both to fade and thin.

To their table now stepped a man whom, my father would later say, when he recounted this story, he looked up at with a shock of recognition. He had never seen the man before, but knew with certainty that there was a link between them.

"So, you're Morgenstern?" the man said, in Yiddish, a vaguely accusing tone in his odd voice that suggested he would not accept a denial.

"Sure," my father said. "And you? I know you, maybe?"

"You know me, no," the man replied, allowing a small lifting at the edge of his lips, lips that were remarkably like my father's own. "I'm your cousin, Rueben, from Montreal." The man was about my father's age, perhaps a few years younger, and, like my father, was of medium height, medium build. He was wearing a dirty wool overcoat, dark blue but with a jaunty red stripe running along the bottom, and rubber galoshes, the buckles undone. He extended his hand. "I asked for you at the paper. A very nice young woman said I might find you here. I worried how I would know you but she said I shouldn't, that I would know you immediately. She was right."

"There is a slight resemblance," my father allowed, reluctant, for reasons he couldn't then fathom, to admit how great it was. "But tell me – Reuben, did you say? How did you even know of me? I knew I had relatives in Montreal, but not their names or anything about them. Yet you knew of me, knew where to find me."

My father's cousin emitted what struck the other two men as a peculiarly mirthless laugh. "Come now, Morgenstern, don't be so modest. People in all directions of the compass read the works of your illustrious father and brother in the pages of *The Morning Journal* and *The Day*. Even in Canada, even in Montreal."

"That I can believe," my father said. "And me?"

Reuben shook his head in protest. "Again, false modesty, cousin. Even you, though you've changed your name, are well known."

Reuben excused himself and went to get a cup of coffee for himself and second cups for my father and Vogel. The two friends exchanged glances. "A flatterer," Vogel said, with obvious distaste. "This one, I don't like the looks of, Morgenstern."

My father laughed. "He looks just like *me*."

"Like brothers," Vogel admitted, tapping his jaw. "But looks like is one thing. It's the look in his eye I don't like."

Reuben returned with the coffees on a tray and sat down. The two cousins exchanged news of their families, and, while my father finished his meal, he learned that his uncle had died but his aunt by marriage still enjoyed her health and that he had half a dozen cousins in addition to Reuben, all grown, most of them still in Montreal. The family business, a furrier shop, had fallen on hard times, however, and had recently closed its doors. When my father pushed aside his tray and lit a cigarette, the cousin leaned forward and lowered his voice. "I could have a private word with you, maybe? It's a matter of...what would you say? Delicacy?"

"Don't mind me," Vogel said, implying that he might merely turn away and not listen, but he rose and joined two other men at a nearby table, Isaac Singer, the novelist, and Jacob Javelit, a compositor at *The Forward*.

"Delicacy means one of two things," my father said, not unkindly. "Women or money. Or both."

His cousin smiled ruefully. Like my father, his hair was starting to recede from his high forehead, and he passed his palm over his skull now in a nervous gesture, patting the hair into place – a gesture my father recognized with a shock as identical to one of his own father's. "Right on both counts. It's taken all my savings to bring us to New York. Things are not so good in Montreal. The shop, as I told you, closed, and I haven't been able to find anything. I hoped things would be better here."

"I might be able to help you find something," my father interrupted. "I know some people."

"That would be wonderful," Reuben said, looking grateful. "In the meantime, there's a place to live to worry about. Food on the table. For myself, I wouldn't ask. I have a wife, a child."

My father allowed himself a moment to think of his own father and the uncle he'd never met, men who had left their families behind while they sought their fortunes in another country. Why would this man take his wife and child with him, he wondered, exposing them to whatever risk there might be? He also thought about Reuben's other options. My father was far from the man's only relative in New York, of course. He thought of his own father, then editor of *The Morning Journal*, who was famous for his frugality. He thought of his older brother, but approaching Sam for a loan would be akin to slamming a door on one's own foot. He thought of his younger brothers, but Izzy had a young wife and two small children of his own and Henry was in law school, and was himself the recipient of occasional assistance from my father. Nathan had moved to Pennsylvania, where he had turned his skill as a silversmith into business, and was rarely heard from. "Certainly I can lend you some money," he said.

"Loan, of course," Reuben said quickly. "I'm not asking for a gift. I'm not asking for charity. It's a loan, and I ask only because of the woman and child. That should be understood."

"Of course," my father said. "Understood. How much do you need?"

Reuben didn't hesitate. "Fifty dollars is the sum I had in mind. Is it too much? We could manage on forty. Fifty would give me more time to find something. It sounds like a lot, maybe..."

My father held up his hand. "That's all right. I can manage fifty. Better that than you should have to borrow somewhere else later, or have to come back to me. I don't have that much with me, of course."

It should be understood that fifty dollars was a fairly large sum of money at the time, what five hundred would be today, or a thousand. But, as it happened, my father was doing well, even though it was only a few months since men in expensive suits had plummeted through the air from tall buildings a short walk from where he now sat. It was an anomaly he would eventually pay for, but, at the depths of the Depression, a few years later, he would be making the princely sum of seventy dollars a week and he earned not far from that now. He lived modestly, in a boarding house, not out of meanness but because of the convenience, and often ate in restaurants, but his tastes were far from expensive. He had no automobile and few women friends, though he had recently made the acquaintance of the woman who would be my mother. What money he did spend was in the cafés and bars of the Lower East Side and along Broadway, at the theatre, which he often frequented, and at the used bookshops along East Broadway and Orchard Street where he would often spend more than he should on a rare edition.

He gave his newly found cousin ten dollars from his wallet and made a date to meet him the next afternoon, after he could make a withdrawal from his bank. Reuben pocketed the money, thanked my father profusely and excused himself. "My wife will be so happy," he said in parting. "It will make her happy to know she's married to a man with generous relatives. Family is worth more than wealth. The Bible got that right."

My father lit another cigarette and drank the last of his coffee, now cold. He looked at his watch. Vogel sat down beside him. "Money?" he asked, his eyelid twitching.

"What else?"

"From that one, Morgenstern, you won't get it back."

"A regular Sigmund Freud you are, such a judge of character."

"Character has nothing to do with it, Morgenstern. Even the Bible says don't lend money. Or borrow it, either."

"Oh ho, Vogel, now you're an expert on the Bible. Have you ever actually seen a copy? I can lend you a nice edition."

"You can laugh, but I don't like the looks of him. You won't get it back."

"You can be so sure, Vogel?"

"From that one? Yes. Besides" – Vogel swatted at his cheek – "with money, you never get it back."

During the following weeks, my father had little reason

to think of his cousin, as he was finding himself increasingly preoccupied with someone else. Not long before the meeting in the Automat, he had attended a gathering of the cutters' union at which Marcantonio, the city's Communist councilman, gave a speech. Afterwards, a klezmer band took the stage, and my father, although he didn't dance, *wouldn't* dance, stayed to have a drink and a bite, to watch the swirling skirts of the girls on the dance floor, before heading to the office to write his story. A man he knew, not that much older than he was, a rabble-rouser in the union named Shally, was there in the company of two attractive young women, and my father approached them with a wink.

"Shally, you're more of a man than I am if you can handle two women at one time."

Shally was ordinarily a sour man with little good to say on any subject, but tonight, in the glow of Marcantonio's speech and the growing sentiment for a strike, he seemed almost merry. He had escaped from a prison in Russia, killing a guard, my father had heard, and had been expelled from both Britain and France for his activities, making him no mere trifler.

"And two more at home, Morgenstern, just as pretty," Shally said slyly.

"You mean these are your daughters?" my father said, with genuine surprise. Shally was the most ordinary looking of men, but the girls, my father thought, were lovely, with flashing eyes and long, wavy hair, one of them a redhead, the other a brunette.

"Sure, they're my daughters. Who else's daughters should they be?"

One of them, the brunette, surprised him further by extending her hand. "I'm Berte," she said. "This is my sister Mars."

My father shook the woman's hand and exchanged a

glance with her that he felt all the way into his shoulder.

"Here," Shally said, wrenching his daughter free from my father's grip, "dance with one of them." With that, he took her in his arms and went spinning off to the circular rhythm of the clarinet, leaving my father standing dumbstruck with the other young woman, the redhead.

"I'm sorry, I, I don't dance," my father stammered. "Let me buy you a drink."

"Come on, one dance won't kill you," the young woman said. Her mouth was very red and she smiled in a wry, lopsided manner.

"No, really, I don't dance," my father said. "I'd kill *you*." He looked over the woman's shoulder in the direction that Shally and his other daughter had spun. "I'm sorry, what did she say her name was?"

"Berte," the sister said, laughing. "*She'll* get you to dance."

A few weeks after they met in the Automat, my father had a telephone call from his cousin inviting him to dinner. Reuben and his small family had taken up residence in a furnished apartment in Brooklyn, a few blocks from Flatbush Avenue, an area my father was familiar with because his brother Izzy had his dental supply shop not too far away. On the appointed evening, he left work at a little after four, bought a bottle of good red wine at a liquor store on East Broadway and strolled slowly towards the subway, enjoying the pleasant early spring air, damp with the melting of a late snow. Even on the dirty, slushy streets of the Lower East Side, redolent with the smells of cooking cabbage and beets and fish, and crowded with people hurrying home for supper, the coming of spring could be sensed, and my father had reason to feel pleased with himself. He took a Lexington Avenue subway to Fourteenth Street, where he transferred to the IRT for the trip under the East River into Brooklyn. When he emerged into the air again, it was already dark and the temperature had dropped a few degrees, forcing him to raise the collar of his raincoat.

Once off Flatbush, the streets, with their trees still bare, were deserted, the buildings narrow, like men standing with their shoulders hunched. He found the address his cousin had provided, a three-story walk-up on Utica Avenue, with no difficulty, and climbed the stairs to the top floor. Reuben opened the door at the first knock, almost as if he had been standing close by, awaiting my father's arrival.

"Morgenstern, come in, come in," he boomed, too heartily, my father thought. "Wine? That's too kind. Let me take your coat. Come, meet the wife."

My father was ushered into the fragrant kitchen and into the presence of a petite, very attractive young woman with blonde hair twisted into a neat bun, and a noticeable bust beneath her modest white shirtwaist and apron. She was standing by the stove, upon which a pot was steaming, a large stirring spoon in her hand. "Morgenstern, my wife, Rachel. Rachel, this is my famous cousin, Harry Morgenstern, our generous benefactor."

"Hardly famous," my father said, surprised to find himself blushing. He offered his hand to the woman, as he had to the dark-haired woman he had met at the dance, but she lowered her eyes shyly and held up the stirring spoon by way of excuse. The aroma of cooking onions brought saliva flooding to his tongue.

"Famous enough," Reuben said, "and certainly our

Dave Margoshes

benefactor."

After the usual pleasantries, the two men retired to the shabby living room, its furniture threadbare and sprung, while the cousin's wife returned to her cooking. The walls were bare of decoration, there was no telephone and there were no toys or articles of children's clothing littering the floor. A bottle of whisky, rye cheaper than my father would ever buy, was produced, and Reuben, who was tieless and in shirtsleeves, poured shots for my father and himself.

"*L'chaim*," he said, raising his glass.

"*L'chaim*," my father repeated, glancing around the dimly lit room.

Through the meal that followed, served on a cloth-covered table in the warm, humid kitchen, there was no sign of and no mention of the couple's child. The furrier job that my father had helped his cousin find had not turned out well and he was again unemployed, but the table conversation was light, filled with talk of the looming strike in the garment trade and anecdotes of life in Montreal, which seemed not all that unlike New York. These latter were related by Reuben in English, in an accent my father realized was as much influenced by French as by Yiddish. The wine he'd brought went well with the fatty pot roast with potatoes and onions Rachel had prepared, which she served with a salad of wilted lettuce and onions tossed with sweetened vinegar, and slices of dark bread, still warm from the oven. Rachel contributed little to the conversation, but she followed it closely with an alert pair of eyes that were a startling shade of green, and, as the meal progressed, her shyness seemed to fade, and she favoured my father several times with a bold, direct glance that, had she not been married, and had he not been interested in the woman he'd met at the dance, would have thrilled him.

"An excellent meal," my father said, finishing his wine and placing a hand over his glass as Reuben proffered the bottle, a few more mouthfuls remaining in the bottom. "I'm curious, Rachel. How is it that your child is so well behaved? When I visit my brother Izzy, his children are all over me. I haven't heard a peep from yours all evening. You have a little girl or a little boy?"

Rachel seemed momentarily confused by my father's question, her face reddening, and her husband quickly interjected: "Oh, our son is with a neighbour. Just for the evening. Yes, we have a son. He's our pride, but he's no better behaved than your brother's children, of that I can assure you. When we have company, we find it's better to have the boy elsewhere."

There was a look in his cousin's eye that immediately recalled for my father Vogel's comment the night they'd met Reuben at the Automat, and for the first time he felt he knew what his friend had meant. He'd already assumed it would be a long time before he saw his fifty dollars again, but that didn't particularly concern him.

"I didn't mean that I minded my nephew and niece," my father said, turning to his cousin's wife, who was gathering up plates.

"No, no, I understand," Reuben said. "But adult talk is better left to adults, don't you agree? Perhaps the next time you honour us with your company."

Rachel served coffee to the two men, who took their cracked and chipped cups and saucers into the living room. No milk or sugar was offered, and my father, sitting in an uncomfortable easy chair, thought better than to request them. The sounds of Rachel moving about the kitchen, pouring a bucket of water heated on the stove into the sink, scraping dishes, punctuated the silence that fell on the room as they sipped the bitter coffee.

"We'll have to do something about finding you another job," my father said eventually.

"That's not necessary, Morgenstern. I have prospects of my own."

"As you wish."

"If it's the money I owe you..."

My father held up a hand. "Believe me, Reuben, that's the farthest thought from my mind."

"Not from mine, I can assure you."

The cousin got up and went to the kitchen door, whispering a few words to his wife in what my father took to be French. When he turned back to his guest, he was rolling down his sleeves and buttoning them. "If you'll excuse me, Morgenstern, I have an appointment right now to speak to a man about a job."

My father, taken by surprise, started to rise but his cousin waved him back into his chair. "Don't go, please. I won't be long. Finish your coffee, at least. Honour my wife with your company."

"If you put it that way, how can I refuse?" my father said, smiling.

Reuben slipped on his suit jacket, its elbows shiny, took the distinctive overcoat with the red stripe from the same doorless closet my father's coat and hat had disappeared into, and, without a further word, left the apartment.

My father, uncertain as to what was expected of him, took a sip of his coffee, then set the cup and saucer down on a rickety coffee table, which was otherwise bare. On an impulse, he rose and strode to the room's one window, which looked out on the deserted street three floors below, lit by the yellow glow of a street lamp, but, even after several minutes, there was no sign of his cousin emerging from the building. Gradually, he became aware that the sounds from the kitchen had ceased, and that he was not alone in the room.

He turned, smiling, starting to speak, "Ah, Rachel," but he was silenced by what he saw. His hostess stood in the kitchen doorway, completely naked, her long blonde hair loosened, her green-eyed gaze directly on him, like a challenge.

"The bedroom's through that way," she said after a moment, nodding her head to the left. "Reuben won't be back for awhile."

My father's eyes fastened on the woman's breasts for a moment, then he tore them away. "What, are you crazy?" he demanded.

"I'm not crazy."

"No? What are you then, if not crazy?"

Rachel gave my father a steady gaze that all but buckled his knees. But neither his will nor his legs faltered.

"I'll tell you what I am," she said. "What I am is ashamed."

She turned away quickly, giving my father an unwanted glimpse of a perfectly rounded behind before she disappeared into the kitchen. The door closed and he heard her moving around behind it, heard what he was sure were muffled sobs.

His impulse was to follow her, to demand an explanation, and, if that was necessary, to comfort her. Instead, he strode to the closet, put on his coat and hat and left the apartment without another word.

He had no expectations as he clattered down the stairs, but, when he came to the bottom landing, there was the man who claimed to be his cousin, smoking a cigarette and faintly smirking.

"You're a crazy man," my father said.

"Sure, I'm crazy. Thinking you would loan me more money, that would be crazy."

"Another loan?" My father was flabbergasted. "Is that what this is about? Money? You *are* crazy."

"Sure, and you would have given it to me, just like that."

"As a matter of fact, I would have," my father said, although, afterwards, he wasn't so sure.

"Just given it to me," Reuben repeated, this time with considerable bitterness, "without making me beg like you did the last time."

My father stared at the man for a moment, at his outstretched palm, then brushed past him, going through a doorway into a narrow outer hall with a filthy tile floor, then through a heavy door and onto a stoop. He stood on the top step for a moment, allowing his eyes to accustom themselves to the darkness, but he didn't want to linger, should Reuben follow him. He plunged down the steps and headed towards the subway station. Around him, Brooklyn hunched like an animal, expectant.

In the early months of World War II, when *The Day* was in its year-long strike and my father was working as a silversmith by day, driving cab at night, and he and my mother were afraid of losing the house they'd built in New Jersey, he went to his brother Henry for a loan. Years later, when he talked about this, he would mention that the sum was forty dollars – all he needed to make the difference between what he had and what he needed for that month's mortgage payment.

Henry said no, offering money problems of his own as an excuse. This was my uncle Henry, my favourite uncle, whom my father had helped to put through law school, who, when I was older, used to pull pennies out of my ears, always had a joke and would gravely advise children to "follow your nose and you won't get lost." My father found the money elsewhere, and he did the next month and the month after, too, but eventually they did lose the house, and they moved me, still an infant, and my sisters into a converted chicken coop not far away.

My father continued to be friendly with his brother, so, if he felt any resentment, he didn't show it. Most likely, any resentment he might have felt would have been directed not at his brother but at himself, not at the one who turned him down but at the one who had asked. Still, it grated him that his own brother had refused him such a small sum. "Forty dollars," he would say to me, with vehemence. Then, grinding out his cigarette: "Neither a borrower nor a lender be."

"Shakespeare," I would say.

"The Bible," he'd reply, smiling. "That was one time the Bible got it right."

Lettres d'amour

The first sigh of love is the last of wisdom.
— *Antoine Bret*

My father, who was a newspaper reporter specializing in labour, was often sent out of town on assignments, usually to cover union conventions. In the first few years of their marriage, well before I was born, these separations, which would take him away for long weekends or even as much as a week, were especially hard on my mother, who had two young children to look after. This was in the Thirties, during the Depression, and the conventions were mostly held in nearby Atlantic City or the Catskills or Poconos. Air travel was not yet popular for most people and the idea of having delegates from the New York and Philadelphia areas travel as far away as Florida was still unknown. "Who even heard of Florida anyway in those days?" my father would later ask. "Just a place for alligators." But there was one extended trip, to Chicago, that took him away for almost two weeks in the spring of 1935, when my sisters were still quite small and my parents had been married recently enough that the length of the separation, for my mother at least, seemed excruciating.

Whenever my father went out of town, my mother wrote him letters, one a day. Usually, because he would only be gone a few days, she didn't mail them – even in those days, when the mail was faster and more reliable than it is today, they wouldn't have reached him in time. She wrote the letters, on sky-blue stationery and using a silver-tipped Shaeffer pen she'd won at college, folded them neatly, inserted them into envelopes that she addressed, in her precise, slanting hand, to "my darling Harry, care of the special place in my heart," and tucked them away in the top drawer of their dresser, where she kept her jewelry box and other things of her own. When he came home, she'd present him with these letters, and he'd read them one a day for the next few days, as if they were actually arriving in the post.

"I bought Esther a new doll," my mother would write, referring to my eldest sister, who was then around four, "and I'm dying to see how she likes it. I didn't give it to her today because I wanted to wrap the box up pretty with paper and ribbons. In the morning, it'll be sitting at her place on the breakfast table."

"So how did Esther like the doll?" my father would ask, although he had, in fact, already seen his darling golden-haired daughter playing with it.

"I can't tell you that," my mother would tease. "You'll have to wait for tomorrow's letter."

In one of these letters, which always contained words of endearment and longing, and often scraps of poetry, my mother closed with these words, "*Je t'aime.*" She had been born in Paris and, though her father, who was on the run from the czar's secret police, took his small family to England before she could speak, she always said that French was her true tongue. She didn't actually learn it until she was in college, but then it came to her as easily as if it had merely been forgotten. Still, she had only two years of study, and little chance to use it after she married my father, so she was far from fluent.

My father's first languages had been Yiddish, which was still his working language, and Polish, long forgotten. He spoke English "like an American," as he said, and could read bits of German, Latin and Greek, which he had taught himself, but could neither read nor speak any French. He knew the phrase she used, though, and he responded one day, when he had occasion to leave her a note, by concluding with another phrase he'd picked up: "*Je t'adore.*"

My mother, jumping to the wrong conclusion, was thrilled. "I didn't realize you knew French," she said.

My father, who didn't approve of lying, wished to avoid the commission. "There's lots about me you still don't know, Bertie," he said obliquely, a knowing smile playing about his lips.

After that, my mother began to pepper her letters to my father with French phrases: *affaire de coeur, billet doux, lettre d'amour, passion grande* and the like. Reading these letters in her presence on his return from a trip, my father would nod knowingly, sometimes getting a sense of the meaning from the context – he was not a linguist by any means, but he had a good feel for language – other times not, but saying nothing or little directly in response. This would not have struck my mother as odd, necessarily, since, as a rule, he didn't comment on everything in her letters, certainly not the idioms, the turns of phrase.

So it was that the harmless deception – no, more a little joke he was having at her expense than a deception, really, that's what he would later explain to us children when this story was told – went undetected and caused no problem for many months. There was still a certain shyness in my mother's relationship with my father, even after several years of marriage and two children, and it's unlikely that she would have dreamed of challenging him, even if a reason to do so had occurred to her. Better, she might have thought, to look the other way.

The trip to Chicago was occasioned by a crisis not only in the garment trades, which were plied by thousands of New Yorkers and so most absorbed my father's attention, but throughout the union movement. The Depression had touched bottom, or so it appeared, and the economy was weakly beginning to raise its head. Roosevelt, who my father thought was a great man, had introduced certain legislation and more was promised. There were stirrings of war in Europe. The soup lines and breadlines were shorter than they had been even a year or two earlier, and the gatherings of men to be found idling in front of the pool halls and saloons along Delancy Street and the Bowery were thinner. There were more jobs, but the pay was as poor as ever, and the mood of the workers and their leaders, who had held their hands and tongues so long, was darkening. Something was changing, something was about to happen – my father said he could smell it in the air as he walked the narrow, cobblestoned streets of the Lower East Side, could hear it ringing in the voices of men. George Meany, the great leader of the American Federation of Labor, had called a meeting of the presidents of the unions of the federation that was to be more like a council of war than a convention in the true sense. The meeting was to last for five days, perhaps more, at the Blackstone Hotel on Chicago's south side, far off the city's beaten path. The press was invited, not to attend the daily sessions themselves, but to wait outside for any pronouncements that might come at the end of each day.

Including the train ride to and fro, my father would be gone for at least a week, perhaps as much as ten days, and he had to borrow a suitcase large enough to accommodate all he would need from his brother Sam, who had travelled in Europe. As she packed his neatly

Dave Margoshes

folded shirts and underwear and his extra suit, complete with wooden hanger, my mother composed a letter in her mind, smiling at the thought of his surprise and pleasure when he opened the suitcase in what she imagined would be a lonely hotel room to find the first of her daily letters, already there. She sat down at the wobbly kitchen table and wrote the letter, beginning, "*Mon cheri*," and ending, as had now become her custom, "*Je t'aime*." In between, since there was really no news to convey, she poured out her love, pride, anxiety and anticipation of loneliness.

"Until you are back in my arms, they will ache with your absence, I will rise in the morning with my arms extended into the shape of you," she wrote, in English. Then, with just a bit of difficulty, in French: "*Seulement par écrit suis-je capable dèxprimer l'énorme de mon amour pour toi, de faire allusion à sa portée, son envergure, sa hauteur, son épaisseur, sa texture, à son bourdonnement. En te parlant, même dans le noir, je perds les moyens de m'èxprimer, je ne suis qu'humilité devant la pureté de ton amour. J'en suis réduite à la simplicité de cette humble phrase: Je t'aime, Berte.*"

My father rode to Chicago in style on the evening Broadway Limited. His newspaper, *The Day*, was prosperous and he was able to afford a bed in a compartment for two, which he shared with his friend and colleague Vogel, who covered labour for the rival *Forward*. On expense allowances, the two of them took their meals in the dining car, drinking French wine from good crystal and stirring real cream into their coffee with sterling silver spoons. Some fifteen years earlier, as a young man seeking his fortune, my father had ridden a similar train to Cleveland, then on to Chicago, then back to Cleveland, where he lived for a several years before returning to New York. On those trips, though, he'd travelled coach, sleeping sitting up in his clothes and sweat, eating salami sandwiches wrapped in wax paper and drinking coffee from a Thermos. "I always wondered what kind of swells rode in the sleepers," he remarked to Vogel.

"Sons of bitches," Vogel said, tapping his ear, a characteristic gesture. "Rich sons of bitches like us."

"Maybe not so rich," my father said.

"All right, don't be so fussy," Vogel said. "*Employed* sons of bitches. You think there's that much of a difference?"

This bit of irony provoked smiles from both men, as they had both prospered during, if not from, the Depression. Circulation of the Yiddish press remained high and both men not only had jobs but relatively well-paying ones.

Another indulgence the two men allowed themselves was a taxicab from the Union Station to the Blackstone Hotel, and my father recalled later that he even tipped the bellhop a quarter, more than double his usual dime. He turned to the unfamiliar suitcase the bellhop had placed on the bed and began to unpack. "*Vus is dus?*" he said aloud, in surprise, as the slim blue envelope, with its familiar handwriting, fell out from between two shirts he was unfolding. The envelope was addressed, as usual, to "my darling Harry," and he sat on the edge of the bed as he read the enclosed letter, not once but twice, not understanding all of it but overcome with emotion nonetheless. He was not a man who believed in any higher power than fate and he said no prayers, but he mumbled something now, a thanks for his great good fortune to whomever or whatever might be listening.

In the bar downstairs, my father spotted Bromberg from *The New York Times* drinking alone. He was an enormous man whose gabardine suits were specially made for him, "by a tentmaker," Vogel liked to say. He was an aloof, cultivated man, not a man to have friends, but he had a slight liking for my father that my father, who admired the man's graceful writing style, cultivated. Vogel, who had an intense dislike for him, was nowhere to be seen so my father approached the *Times* man. "Bromberg, may I join you?" he asked.

"Certainly, Morgenstern," the fat man replied, lifting his funnel-shaped amber glass. "The draught is exceptionally good. It's German." He smiled sheepishly and waved his free hand in a gesture that seemed to indicate a mixture of embarrassment and resignation.

My father signalled to the barman and sat down. Bromberg seemed unusually friendly, perhaps because the two men were so far from home, and my father, on impulse, pulled out my mother's letter. "How's your French, Bromberg?"

"Good," Bromberg said sharply, as if annoyed at the question. He had travelled widely in Europe and my father had seen him at meetings they both were covering reading slim volumes of poetry in French.

"If you can avoid looking at the English passages, I'd appreciate it," my father said. "It's the French I'm interested in." He neatly folded the letter so that only the paragraph in question was face up and handed it to Bromberg. He felt awkward but was dying to know what my mother had written.

Bromberg looked at the letter, up at my father and down at the letter again. He set his glass of beer on the table and brought the letter closer to his face, squinting slightly. "The light here..."

"Maybe later would be better..."

"No, that's fine." Bromberg nodded his head slightly as he read, his thick, puckered lips moving almost imperceptibly, as if he were in prayer, until they spread into a broad smile. "Morgenstern, a jewel like you should ask for a raise. You can't possibly be getting as much as you deserve."

"A jewel?"

"That's what this woman thinks you are."

My father hesitated, embarrassed. "What does she say?"

Bromberg waved the letter airily before bringing it close to his face again. "This may not be it exactly, but something like this:

"'Only on paper is it possible for me to express the enormity of my love for you, to hint at its scope, its breadth and width and height, its thickness, its texture, the hum it makes.'" Bromberg raised his eyes to interject, "This is some admirer you have, Morgenstern. Sorry." He resumed his translation: "'Speaking to you, even in the dark, my powers with words are crippled, I am humbled by the purity of your love. I am reduced to the simplicity of this humble phrase: I love you.'"

There was silence after Bromberg finished reading. The two men sipped their beers. My father glanced at the clock over the bar – there was still an hour before they were to be at the dinner which would open the gathering. "I have another favour to ask," he finally said.

Late that night, after he had telephoned his story of the evening's activities to New York, my father sat at the table in his room in his undershirt, carefully copying the words that Bromberg had written for him on a

Dave Margoshes

napkin. His handwriting was always poor and now, slightly drunk, it was bad enough that he felt the need to copy out the letter a second time. "It was a thrill to find your letter amidst my shirts and underwear," he wrote, in English. "A thousand miles or ten, it doesn't matter how much geography is between us, how many railroad ties, we could not be closer. Your words pierce me like arrows, going straight to my heart, the sweetness of your smile racing through my veins."

Here, he switched to the words Bromberg had written as he had dictated: "*Jusqu'à ce que je te tienne à nouveau dans mes bras, crois bien que je suis à toi et à toi seule, que mon coeur n'appartient qu'à toi.*"

He looked at the strange words until his vision began to swim, trying to make sense of them. He noted the *toi* repeated over again and knew it was "you," saw with a momentary blush the *bras* but knew it meant "arms," recognized *Je suis* as "I am" and *coeur* as "heart." That much French he knew. To reassure himself, he checked the other side of the napkin, where he had written the message to be translated, pronouncing the words aloud: "Until I hold you again in my arms, believe that I am yours and yours alone, that my heart belongs only to you."

Satisfied, he sealed and stamped an envelope printed with the hotel's return address and padded in his socked feet down the hall to the brass mail chute beside the silent elevator. "Good night love," he whispered as he dropped the letter through the lidded slot, thinking that it was an hour later in New York and that my mother might well be up at this hour, feeding the baby, that she would feel his thought.

In the morning, when he came down to breakfast, there was a letter from her awaiting him at the front desk, written and posted the same day he left the city.

"How I await your reply to my letter," she wrote, the slanted rhythm of her hand pulling him immediately into the universe of her blue stationery and washing him over with an immense feeling of loneliness. And in French: *"Comme je me languis de tes mains, de ta parole, de tes lèvres sur les miennes."* Then, in English again, "The children, too, miss you. Esther spent all afternoon drawing you a picture of our building so you'd remember where you're to return to."

And sure enough, folded in with the letter, was a large sheet of scrap newsprint scribbled over with crayons: a tall rectangle studded with small squares, on one side the ocean, on the other railroad tracks leading off the page and a locomotive with an engineer in a striped hat. In one of the squares was a blonde smiling face and a waving arm, Esther herself. The drawing was bordered with hearts and Xs for kisses. "Look at this, Vogel," my father said, handing the drawing over the breakfast table. "I've told you a hundred times you should have a wife and children."

"What woman would have me as a husband?" Vogel said sourly over the lip of his coffee cup. "What child would have me as a father?"

My father smiled tolerantly and turned his attention to a napkin, upon which he scrawled *"My darling, it's been mere hours since your letter but already the hours hang heavy as I wait for the next."*

At lunchtime, my father conferred with Bromberg, who came up with this translation: *"Ma chérie, il ne s'est passé que quelques heures depuis ta dernière lettre et déjà les heures me pèsent dans l'attente de la prochaine. Quant à toi, j'en suis sûr, beaucoup de choses te tiennent occupée et tu ne penses pas à moi."*

My father glanced at what the other man had carefully printed out and shook his head with wonder. "So many words."

"Yes," Bromberg agreed, "the French are verbose. Never one word when two will do."

The following day's letter contained another drawing by my sister, more outpourings of passion and tenderness in both English and French and, because it was written the day after his departure, was filled with household news: Esther's skinned knee, Judy's colic, a letter from the bank. By the end of the week, though most of his time was devoted to the events unfolding around him, with declarations of war on the business world and news of strategies emerging daily from the summit, through either official pronouncements or unofficial leaks, my father's head was plugged with such family trivia and his ears rang with the musicality of French phrases conveying promises, pledges, entreaties, enticements. And Bromberg, who continued to be amused by his assignment, had been drawn closer and closer into what my father now felt had become a conspiracy of sorts.

Each afternoon at three, the two men would meet in the hotel bar and Bromberg would translate whatever French passages there might be in that day's letter from my mother, reading them out loud in a cultivated voice that retained, after the four years the enormous man had spent at Harvard, only the faintest traces of his upbringing in the Bronx. Then my father would dictate a few sentences or two of reply and Bromberg, scribbling on a napkin or the back of an envelope, would produce a version in French. There was some trust involved, as my father had no way of knowing for certain what his colleague wrote, but he was confident that Bromberg's command of spelling, grammar, diction and syntax in French were impeccable. What was there to be concerned with?

On Friday, with just one or, at the most, two days left to the labour summit, an unexpected note of alarm crept into my mother's daily letter. "My darling Harry," she began as always, "I was surprised by the tone you took in your response to my news about Judy's recurring cough. I assure you I'm not being overly protective." This puzzled my father since he recalled no accusations, and certainly no tone, in the letter he'd written two days earlier – or was it three? Suddenly he was confused about how long it took letters to go from New York to Chicago and back again. This letter was dated Thursday, so should be responding to what he had written Wednesday, but perhaps it was Tuesday. Had he taken such a tone on Tuesday? It was so far back, and so much had transpired at the meeting since then, he couldn't be sure. At any rate, the crossness of my mother's own tone immediately disappeared as she turned to other subjects, so he gave it no further thought. And if her passages in French, when Bromberg translated them for him that afternoon, were briefer and seemed less passionate, that surely was his imagination playing tricks on him.

Nevertheless, in his letter to her that night, he began by writing "Dearest Bertie, I apologize a thousand times if anything I may have said gave you offense or hurt your feelings. It was certainly unintentional and perhaps attributable to the tense atmosphere here at the hotel." And he'd already made certain that the passages he dictated to Bromberg for translation into French, which he now carefully copied out, were especially affectionate. Bromberg, he recalled, had nodded his head in approval as he scribbled.

The following day, Saturday, there was no letter from my mother. My father, surprised, exclaimed: "Surely there's mail delivery on Saturday in Chicago," to which the desk clerk assured him there was, though only one, in the morning. There would be no further delivery until Monday morning. But by that time, my father knew, he would be on his way home, as it now seemed certain the summit would conclude Sunday afternoon, carefully timed to make the headlines of Monday morning's newspapers. There would be a pickup at noon, however, the desk clerk told him, and though he wasn't sure if a letter he posted today would get home before him or afterward, he sought out Bromberg after breakfast and dictated one final message in French. "I love you and count the minutes, the seconds, until once again I hold you in my arms," he dictated, blushing. He realized with sudden horror how deeply he had opened himself to the other man's scrutiny, but it was too late now for modesty. "Until then," he went on, his voice trembling with emotion, "I will be only a shadow of myself, a hollow man, waiting to be filled once again by the sweet liquor of your love."

Bromberg raised his heavy head and gave my father a frank look, and smiled with satisfaction as he returned to his task, his jowls quivering. "You're a poet, Morgenstern," he said, "a blessed poet."

That evening, there was a banquet, thrown by the Illinois branch of the federation, and the Blackstone Hotel's best hall was filled with the cream of the leadership of the state's unions. Meany gave one of his trademark thunderous speeches, though he omitted most of the key announcements, which were being held for the following day. Afterwards, there was much drinking and when my father went to bed he barely had time to whisper "Goodnight, darling Bertie" to his pillow before he was asleep. The following day, as he had expected, there was a press conference shortly after noon, but there had been enough leaks that my father already had most of his story written. A few quotes pasted in and he was ready to dictate into the telephone to the rewrite man awaiting his call on the city desk in New York. Afterwards, there was plenty of time to pack, and he and Vogel shared a taxi to Union Station. That night, he slept on the crisp sheets of a Pullman berth dreaming of his own bed.

Once back in the city on Monday morning, the expense account clicked off and my father took the subway from Penn Station to Coney Island, where my parents had a small apartment on West Twenty-First Street near Surf Avenue, within scent if not sight of the ocean. He lugged the big suitcase up the two flights of stairs and paused outside the door to catch his breath before turning the key. "Bertie, children, I'm home," he called. There was no response. My father put the suitcase down and walked down the narrow hallway to the kitchen. Dishes were in the sink but there was no other sign of life. "Bertie?" he called again.

He found my mother in their bedroom standing by the window. She didn't turn when he called her name from the doorway and he could see from the movement of her shoulders that she was crying. "Bertie, what on earth?"

He took her by the shoulders and turned her around. Her eyes and nose were red and her cheeks glistened. "You're a h-h-h-horrible man," she managed to hiccup out.

My father was dumbstruck. In the five years they'd been married they'd had arguments, even one memorable fight, and there had certainly been tears before, but nothing like this, the cause so completely mysterious. "What are you talking about, Bertie?" he demanded.

"What I'm talking about? The terrible things *you*

said. The vile things you wrote about your own children, and about me, all week." She paused to blow her nose with a handkerchief she had balled in her hand. "And today's letter...oh, Harry, how could you do such things? How could you tell me about those women?"

My father looked at her with amazement. At first, it seemed to him that she was speaking nonsense but gradually it began to dawn on him what might have happened. "I said things? When? Where?"

"In your l-l-l-letters," my mother hiccuped. "Your *horrible* letters."

"In my letters...I said these terrible things in French?"

"Yes," she spit out. "That made it all the worse." She gave him then a pointed look, as if she too were perhaps beginning to understand.

"Bertie, Bertie," my father crooned, stroking my mother's auburn hair, which, at the time, she wore loose around her shoulders. "I have a confession to make." Later, he would think about what he would have to say to Bromberg. And whether a punch in the fat, malicious bastard's nose would be appropriate. As for now, it was enough that she was in his arms.

From that day on, he determined, there would be no more French spoken in his house, no more French in their letters, no more secrets, no more deceptions, harmless or not – *harmless!* – no more lies, white or any other kind.

Outside the bedroom window, on the street below, children were playing. Through the glass, my parents could hear the muffled sound of their shouts, but not the words.

A Bargain

My father used to say that my mother was the one in the family who wore the pants. As he said it, he would invariably be wearing pants himself, either the pants of his suit or a pair of the Sears catalogue blue jeans my mother ordered for him, and she would be wearing one of her many floral-print skirts, so the remark was surely meant to be ironic, though at the time, and until I went off to college and learned its delicious meaning, irony was a concept I was unfamiliar with, and what my father said was merely puzzling. The closest my mother ever came to wearing pants was the voluminous denim culottes she put on to tend her garden in the summer. Beyond those, and the one-piece swimsuit she wore when we went to the beach, I never saw her out of a skirt or dress, though she would occasionally walk around the house in her slip for a while after coming home from work. She was never embarrassed to be dressed that way in front of me, and so I in turn was never embarrassed to see her.

I think what my father meant by the remark was that my mother made all the big decisions in their life together. Another of his favourite remarks – again, ironically – was that he made the *big* decisions, on war and peace, world hunger, the economy and other weighty matters, while my mother contented herself with the *small* decisions, those related to the family and household, things like spending money, feeding and clothing them and the children, what movie to go to and so on. My father also often said that he and my mother did everything around the house together, with him doing the physical labour and my mother "supervising," if it was something to do with the outside, and her doing the work and him supervising if it was inside – chores like the dishes and the laundry. All of these comments – conveyed in a joking voice but with a serious undertone – related to my father's often-expressed grievance that my mother was "bossy."

It was true that she almost always got her way. But not always. My father liked a drink now and then, meaning several times a day. I don't know how many. She would have liked him not to drink at all. His concession to her was rarely to drink his preferred rye whisky in her presence – never at home, but he would let his guard down and have one or two at family gatherings where liquor was flowing. "I'm just doing this to be polite," he would say, a little too loudly but usually with a wink, and the uncles would smile. But he kept a flask in the inside pocket of his overcoat – and when, a few years later, he became a commuter, another in the glove compartment of his car. There was also a bottle in the bottom drawer of his desk at work, and during the course of his day he made occasional stops at barrooms where he was a familiar customer. At home, at night, usually seated at the kitchen table in his undershirt, he would have a glass or two of sherry or port, usually the cheapest brands. My mother bought it for him, and that's what he specified, the cheapest, which, I imagine, also appealed to her own sense of frugality. This was her concession to him, these fortified wines, "a gentleman's drink," he would say when he unscrewed the bottle, as if to imply it was no drink at all then, and didn't count.

Dave Margoshes

Although I was a witness to them all through my growing up, this to-ing and fro-ing, these nuances of their life together, it wasn't until I was grown and involved in a relationship of my own that I came to understand the delicate balance they had constructed and maintained. Well, not understand, but begin to.

Long before that, before my birth even, my father had a bad experience with drink, so bad that, even though he did not give up drinking, he vowed he would never again be drunk, really drunk, in that state where he could not count on his own abilities or judgment, where he was of no use to anyone.

I heard about this experience, as might be expected, after I had my own first bad encounter with drink, when I was seventeen, drank too many illicit beers while out with my friends, and, on the way home, indelicately put the family car in the narrow river branch that ran alongside the road that led to our place in the country, where we'd finally moved the year before – a return to rural life my parents had quit when my sisters were approaching college age. This was the finest car we had ever owned, a Lincoln less than ten years old, with leather seats and power windows, which we had purchased cheaply the year before from my mother's sister Mars, who was married to a lawyer and so the best off of her siblings, and I was terrified that I'd damaged it, more frightened of that than what might happen to me – in the split second that the car was airborne before landing in the shallow water, I issued a silent prayer that *I* pay whatever price might be due, not the car.

But, miraculously, I wasn't hurt, and even the car received only a minimum of damage, the mud it settled into more an affront to the Lincoln's dignity than anything else. Really, what happened to me was not exceptional; what was memorable was the story my father told me afterwards.

My parents and my two sisters lived in an apartment on West Twenty-First Street, near the corner of Surf Avenue, in Brooklyn, Coney Island to be more exact, not within sight but, as my father put it, within smelling distance of the ocean. From their living room window, which faced south, they could see the top of the Parachute Jump on the Boardwalk and, in the summer, hear the shrieks of riders on the Cyclone. My mother was left alone every day with the children, both of them still too young even for kindergarten, while my father escaped to his own world of work, first riding the Surf Avenue bus, then descending into the dark cavern of the Stillwell Avenue subway station and emerging within half an hour on the Lower East Side of Manhattan at the East Broadway station, a short walk to *The Day*. "If anyone needed a drink," my father said, "it was her, not me." My mother, for reasons of her own, rarely drank more than a few sips from a glass of wine at family events. But my father, as I've said, kept a bottle in the drawer of his desk, even in those early days, and he had a drink from it as soon as he arrived at work, presumably to brace himself for the rigours that lay ahead. Later he would have a drink or two with lunch, and another drink or two with some cronies before catching the subway for the return trip to Coney Island. Walking home from the bus, he would often stop at a tavern on the corner of Mermaid Avenue and Twenty-First Street for a glass of beer – which he believed would hide the odour of whisky on his breath – before tackling the three flights of stairs that led to wife and children with whom, almost always, he would be loving husband and father, revealing no sign of the alcohol he'd consumed during the day other than a mellow disposition. My father had a temper, but he rarely displayed it.

On the night in question, though, a brisk, overcast night in late March, 1936, my father had had one or two drinks too many. He had a meeting to cover, so didn't go home at the usual time for dinner and the evening with his family. Instead, he had dinner and several drinks with his good friend Vogel, his counterpart at *The Forward*. The two men then attended the meeting, a boisterous gathering of the membership of Local 37 of the Ladies' Garment Workers' Union, which was then locked in negotiations with the owners of the garment district dress factories that lined lower Seventh Avenue. Afterwards, my father went back to the office to write his story, in which he reported that a strike was imminent, again taking a drink or two from the bottle in his drawer. By the time he climbed the steps to the Coney Island apartment, stopping at each landing to catch his breath, he was weary and unsteady on his feet. His fingers were chilled and he fumbled with the key.

Covering meetings and coming home late was not unusual for my father – he would do it at least once a week, often twice. Usually, he would creep into a dark apartment, its silence punctuated only by the steady breathing of my mother and sisters in sleep and the occasional groan from the pipes, and he would undress quietly in the dark and slip into the warm bed without causing any disturbance, marvelling at his good fortune – that he had a comfortable home to come home to, a loving wife, darling children, things that, only a few years earlier, he had thought had somehow permanently eluded him, that he had grown too old for.

On this particular night, though, the lights were on when he opened the door, and even through his blurry eyes he could tell immediately that something was not right.

"Bertie?" my father called.

My mother came out of the bathroom into the entrance hall. The front of her housecoat was drenched, her hair was in disarray and her face was flushed. "Oh, Harry, thank goodness you're here. Esther's sick."

My sister Esther, ten years older than me, was then not yet five. She had been out of sorts that morning when my father left for work, with a mild fever and complaining that her head hurt. This was obviously something more serious.

My father said nothing for a moment and my mother continued: "She's burning up with fever. I've got her in the tub, cooling her off. We really have to take her to the hospital."

"Of course," my father said. He and my mother shared a brief hug of reassurance, and he turned his head so she wouldn't smell the alcohol on his breath, though she was quite used to it.

Then my father turned to go into the bathroom, shedding his overcoat. My sister Esther is fair, with blue eyes and dirty blonde hair that, in childhood, was quite pale. Her hair was long and usually tied into braids, but on this day, because of her headache, my mother had left it loose; now, it was bunched up into a loosely fitting bathing cap, lending her a slightly comical look. She lay on her back in a tub half filled with cool water, naked and pale as the belly of a fish except for her face, which was flushed bright red. My father stood in the doorway, frozen, for what was only a moment but seemed to him like an intolerably long time, taking this in. She was awake, with tears dribbling down her enflamed cheeks, but her mouth formed a small smile. "Hello, Daddy," she said weakly.

My father felt a flash of shame, his trance breaking.

"My god," he said, "Esthella, baby, it's all right, we're going to get you to a doctor," then he stepped forward, intending to get down on his knee beside the tub.

The bathroom floor was wet. A crumpled towel lay beside the tub where my mother had been kneeling as she sponged Esther before my father's return. As he stepped forward, his right foot landed on the towel, which slid forward. My father teetered for a moment, then fell with a crash onto the floor, banging his left shoulder against the tub. He shouted out an obscenity, something he rarely did and never in front of his wife or children. Pain stabbed through his shoulder and, even worse, his ankle, which had twisted sideways as he fell.

"Harry, my god, are you okay?" my mother cried. She raced into the bathroom, narrowly avoided slipping on the wet floor herself, and knelt beside him. My father, already starting to get to his feet, brushed her aside. "I'm okay, Bertie. It's nothing."

The whole thing, start to finish, had taken only seconds, but my father knew it wasn't nothing. His ankle was seriously twisted and the pain that raced up his leg as he placed weight on it was excruciating. But the pain served one useful purpose, clearing my father's head.

"Get her dressed," he told my mother. "I'll call a taxi."

Ten minutes later, my mother and father emerged from the doorway of their apartment building with Esther, dressed and wrapped in a blanket, whimpering in my father's arms. My mother held my sister Judy, who was not yet three; there was no one with whom she could be left, so they had no choice but to rouse her protesting from sleep and take her along. My father's shoulder was aching with dull pain – putting his coat back on had been agonizing – but was bearable, even with his daughter's slight weight; his ankle, though, fired hot bright bolts of pain through his leg with every limping step. Rain had started to fall and they stood in the shelter of the doorway for a minute as they waited for the taxi. He pressed his hand against Esther's burning forehead and whispered into her ear, "It's okay, Esthella, Daddy's got you, it's okay."

My father had no idea whether his daughter's situation was serious or slight, but he feared the worst. Being a devout atheist, he had no god to direct prayers to, but that didn't prevent him from composing them on occasion, and in that brief pause in the doorway, he proposed a bargain with the universe. If only Esther would be spared, he would never again allow himself to be so drunk – as drunk as he'd been that night, so drunk that he had done himself harm, that he had delayed, not thought clearly, even if only for a few moments; so drunk that he might have done others harm – never again would he allow himself to be that way.

Then the taxi was there, they were in it and on their way, my father grateful to be off his feet, the cab's windshield wipers clacking away thought.

Coney Island Hospital was just a few minutes away on Ocean Parkway near Avenue Z. Judy had been born there and my parents knew it well. The taxi pulled up at the emergency entrance and my mother, who had sat Judy down on the seat between her and my father, got out and came around the car to open my father's door. He stumbled out, gasping, Esther pressed tightly against his chest. For a moment he teetered, and was sure his leg would collapse under him, but he shot out his left hand to steady himself against the door of the taxi, that motion reigniting the pain in his shoulder. Esther shifted in his arms, threatening to slip from his grip, but once he had righted himself he was able to pull his left arm back in, redistributing her weight in time. He didn't think about his wife and other daughter, about the cab driver and the fare, but concentrated all his attention on the hospital door, which was swinging open, a white-uniformed nurse pushing a wheelchair appearing through it like one of the angels he had read about as a boy, welcoming them to heaven.

"She's burning up," my father croaked, surrendering his first-born into the nurse's arms.

In another ten minutes my father sat in the same wheelchair gritting his teeth as an intern pried off his heavy black shoe and began to manipulate his ankle, already swollen to almost twice its normal size. Every movement of the doctor's hands sent excruciating pain flooding through my father's lower body. My mother and Esther had disappeared through a curtained doorway with another doctor, and Judy, cranky and snivelling, had been taken by a nurse to a small room with colouring books and a cot. "Don't worry, she'll be fine, won't you, honey," the nurse said. My father had tried to follow my mother and Esther but was met with similar assurances and worried frowns over his limp. A nurse with a thin line of perspiration on her upper lip like a faint moustache had pushed him down into the wheelchair and there he sat for a few minutes waiting, his entire body now throbbing, the pain in his ankle scorching up through his right leg and into his pelvis, the pain in his shoulder radiating down his arm, all the way to his fingers. His throat burned and even his head was aching, locked in a tight grip that pressed against his temples, keeping thought at bay, though he remained conscious of the steady stream of doctors and nurses coming in and out of the room that my mother and Esther had been taken into, their faces unreadable.

An intern in a white jacket, a man who looked little older than the teenaged boy who ran errands in my father's office, materialized in front of him, immediately sinking to his knees.

"This looks really nasty," the intern said. He composed his face to express seriousness, but it couldn't completely mask delight. My father grimaced in response. "I don't suppose you've got a drink, some whisky, maybe?"

The intern let his grin emerge. He wore a wispy moustache, obviously grown to make him appear older. "You find some, I'll join you. In the meantime, relax." He stood up and probed the muscles in my father's shoulder with unsympathetic fingers. "You're holding yourself so tight, you're just making this worse."

My father slumped with exhaustion as he was wheeled to have X-rays taken – the intern was right, when he willed his muscles to loosen, the pain in his shoulder began to subside. Even the ache in his head seemed to lessen.

While he waited for the technician to adjust his equipment, my father gazed through a rain-stained window at darkness softened by the glow of an exterior light. He could see an ambulance driving into the frame of the window, then disappearing from view, the frame going dark again. He thought of the bargain he had proposed, just minutes earlier, and renewed it. Never again, he thought. He had offered up such bargains to the gods of the universe before, with smaller stakes, over smaller matters, and then proceeded to forget them, to let his end down, he knew that. But this was different, this time he meant it, and he assumed his intention and resolve were clear.

The X-rays showed the injury to my father's shoulder to be no more than a bad bruise. He was given an ice pack, and then the doctor and nurse forgot about it. But the ankle turned out to be more than sprained. It was broken and would need to be set painfully and placed in a plaster of Paris cast. First he was told that someone, a specialist, was being telephoned and would be there within an hour, then that another emergency had precluded that; he would have to wait until morning. It was now way past midnight, so he would just have to grit his teeth and endure the pain for another six hours or more, the intern cheerfully told him. "It's only pain," he said.

My father took some grim satisfaction in this development, interpreting it to mean that the universe – or whatever was out there – had accepted his bargain, or had perhaps upped the ante slightly, that his condition should be worse so that his child's could be better. And it was. My mother soon joined him, relief clear on her face. Esther's fever was already down, and she was asleep. They would keep her overnight and watch her, but the doctor didn't think it was anything too serious. "Just one of those mysterious childhood things," he said, a diagnosis he was obviously satisfied with. My father nodded his head in agreement. It was hard to be an atheist when the universe operated with such apparent purpose.

Years later, my father would only remember that Esther had been burning up with fever and had thrown her parents into a panic. Perhaps, as the doctor had suggested, it had just been one of those baffling childhood ailments that come and go without apparent explanation, leaving no discernible mark.

My father was changed, though, or so he believed.

He recalled that my mother looked in on Judy, who was sleeping peacefully on a cot in the playroom, and then went to fetch two coffees in paper cups while my father sat in a strangely calm repose and communed with the pain in his ankle. The coffee when it came, hot and milky, would be soothing in its own way, and would suffice to stifle his craving for something stronger. But there was a brief period after the intern left, when all the nurses were busying themselves elsewhere and my mother had not yet returned, that he was alone with his demons in a small bare room, his leg extended. They had given him morphine and the pain was retreating in almost noticeable waves, like soldiers quitting a battlefield. The muting of the pain served, though, to make his desire for both a drink and a cigarette more acute. His body cried out for both. There were sure to be cigarettes in his jacket pocket and a small flask, half full of rye whisky, in the inside breast pocket of his coat. He didn't know what had become of either. When my mother came back, he would ask her to find his jacket and bring him a cigarette – surely there could be no objection to that. As for the flask, no, he would forego that. Yes, he had promised only that he wouldn't again be drunk, not that he would never drink again, like converted sinners caught up in religious fervour who vowed never to touch another drop. A drink now, he felt certain, would not be a breach of the bargain he had made, it would not put Esther in jeopardy, would not compromise his word. Still, he thought, it was better to be safe. He had been careless, he knew, just that, but that was bad enough. He would try not to be careless again.

Music by Rodgers, Lyrics by Hart

These days, envelopes come to my house almost weekly offering to make me a millionaire. All I have to do is open them and look inside; I may already be a winner.

I never am, and I've largely stopped looking, but these letters remind me of a time when my mother and her friend Moishe Cahan entered magazine and grocery store contests with a vengeance, the same sort of grim determination that drives a gambler to the slot machines and card tables.

My father took a dim view of these pursuits. "This is foolishness, Bertie," he would complain, a hand-rolled cigarette burning in the ashtray and the first of his several evening glasses of port or sherry in front of him on the chipped Formica kitchen table, as my mother, still in her housedress and apron, sat across from him, the dark curls that adorned her head falling over her brow as she scribbled furiously in a steno pad, making rhymes. "Flour, hour, our, scour, dour, power," she was writing in the light blue ink she favoured, using the silver-tipped pen she'd won in college for high marks in French. In my father's moral lexicon, *foolishness* was one of the worst sins a person could fall prey to, even worse than larceny, which could perhaps be explained by need – hungry children, for example. Foolishness was a moral failure for which its author could have only himself to blame. He would never have thought of my mother as a fool, but he did believe some of her actions were foolish, and was always quick to say so. The contests she pursued, the jingles and slogans she composed, clearly fell into that category in his view.

"But what does it hurt?" my mother asked absently, brushing away a lock of chestnut hair as she looked up. She gave my father a crooked little smile, half innocence, half impudence. "Is my jingle any more foolish than your sherry? Now really."

My father, who was a newspaper reporter, was employed all through the Depression, actually made a good wage, and had no desperate need for instant riches; neither, of course, did my mother, but, as a young mother with first one, then two small children at home, and my father gone all day and often into the evening, she did have a craving for diversion.

Moishe, on the other hand, was in conspicuously dire straits. The Crash had come during his final year of architecture school, forcing him to drop out. He worked sporadically as a draftsman – an occupation he would sourly continue with when times got better – but mostly he was unemployed, disappointed and at loose ends, in need of something to do with his restless, bird-like hands. His wife, Rachel, who had been my mother's best friend since high school, also had two young children to look after, but her poetic, abstract mind didn't lend itself to the riddles, puzzles and other concrete challenges of the magazine and radio contests that attracted her husband and my mother, though she didn't frown on them the way my father did.

There were certain expenses involved which, because my parents had money and the Cahans didn't, my mother undertook to cover. These were postage, of course, but also the purchasing of certain products: labels had to be scissored from cereal boxes and flour sacks, protective seals gingerly snipped from beneath the lids of peanut butter, jam and pickle jars. My mother could rationalize these purchases easily enough – she had to shop anyway, and most of the products were ones she might well have bought, contest or no, though not always in such large numbers. But it wasn't the money my father begrudged, or even, since he wasn't the jealous sort, the growing intensity of the relationship between my mother and her friend's husband, the two of them sitting at the kitchen table in the Cahans' cramped apartment in the Bronx, near the Grand Concourse, or at my parents' only slightly larger place in Coney Island, their heads close together as they pored over pencil and paper or some reference book, or falling helplessly together on the carpeted living room floor in bursts of giggles as they laboured over a limerick or a jingle while my father and Rachel, who had been attempting to carry on a conversation, looked on with slightly amused expressions; no, it was the wasted time he thought was foolishness, especially since, in his view, the chances of them actually winning anything was highly unlikely, the contests being either rigged or impossible. Testimonials in the magazines from previous winners he always dismissed as "cock-and-bull stories." Earlier in his career, in Cleveland, he had written the *bintel briefs*, the advice to the lovelorn column, and no one knew better than he how little one could rely on what one read.

"But it's *my* time," my mother responded when my father complained of the hours she spent thumbing through dictionaries, encyclopedias and the thesaurus out of which the answers to puzzles and the rhymes for jingles emerged. Although it seemed frustratingly impossible that he might actually sell any, Moishe had even taken on a commission job as an encyclopedia salesman to give them access to more reference books, and many of these works were stacked on the coffee table in the living room and on the kitchen counter of my parents' apartment, just as they must have been in the Cahans'. "And what *else* should I be doing with my time, Harry? I can't wash and fold diapers *all* day long."

My mother had spent two years at Hunter College before she married, and her education was one thing my father, who had only gone as far as the fifth grade and was largely self-taught, *was* jealous of; it was a matter of great pride to him that he had come so far, that he made his living writing, with so little schooling, and it irritated him that she didn't take more advantage of what she had. Never mind that her education, and Moishe's even greater one, were great assets in their pursuit of the contests, where knowledge of things as trivial as the states' capitals and as arcane as Greek myth and European history could be invaluable; he would have liked to have seen her writing poetry, which Rachel Cahan did, or reading serious books, like the Freud and Shakespeare he himself was partial to, to improve her mind, not reference works in hopes of winning some money – "filthy lucre," he sneered – or a new stove or living room ensemble.

In fact, my mother *did* write poems, and after her death my sisters and I found some of them, folded and bound with a blue velvet ribbon along with love letters she and my father had written to each other during their occasional separations in their early years together, when my father, who covered the labour beat, would travel out of town on stories.

As it happened, he was away on just such a trip when my mother and her friend finally won a contest.

Dave Margoshes

As he did every summer, my father went to Atlantic City that year, 1936, to cover the Ladies' Garment Workers' Union convention. He was gone for barely more than a week, but in the six letters my mother wrote to him (four mailed, including two that came back after his return, marked "addressee no longer here," and two left unmailed for him to read on his return), she expressed such longing that it might have been a month, or a year. These letters were all written in English, my parents having forsworn French after the painful misunderstanding of a year earlier. She felt, she wrote on the third day, "like the wife of a seafarer, one of those whaling men or merchant marines who would be at sea for years on end, while their families lived their own closeted lives in Liverpool or New Bedford. It's only the boardwalk at Coney Island, and I know your feet are walking on a similar boardwalk no more than a hundred miles from here, but I feel like I'm on one of those legendary widow's walks, my face wet with a mixture of sea spray and tears." This from a woman whose parents had both been born in central Russia, far from any large body of water, though she herself was born in Paris and crossed both the English Channel and the Atlantic before she was four years old. How my father could say she was wasting her education when she was capable of hyperbole like that, I don't know.

It was during my father's absence that my mother and Moishe got word that their efforts had finally paid off.

The contest in which they had success was sponsored by a flour company and involved the writing of a jingle – the winning entry was to be professionally produced and become part of the company's radio advertising campaign. More importantly, first prize was five thousand dollars – an enormous sum in those days –

and a cruise to the South Seas; though it's hard to imagine such pleasure cruises continued through those Depression years, apparently they did. The jingle my mother and Moishe wrote is lost, so I can't record it here; they didn't win first prize, and their contribution was never used by the flour company. They did win third prize, though, which was one thousand dollars, a set of stainless steel pots and pans and other kitchen paraphernalia and a certificate redeemable at the grocer's for up to one hundred dollars worth of selected food products.

When my father came home from his trip, on Sunday evening, he was greeted by a nearly hysterical wife, two overexcited small children and a kitchen that looked, he used to say, like it had been hit by a tornado: the sink was filled with dirty dishes, the countertops were crowded with more dishes, open jars and boxes of food, the floor was filthy, particularly in one corner where a suspiciously fragrant stain still glistened. This was so unusual that he immediately assumed some calamity had befallen his family in his absence.

"Where were you?" my mother demanded. "I phoned and couldn't reach you."

"Bertie, what's happened?" my father gasped in reply, genuinely alarmed.

"I tried to ph-ph-ph-phone you," my mother stammered, tears streaming down her face. "No one knew where you were." First she hugged my father, then she stepped back and began to beat his chest with her hands. He allowed her to do this for a few seconds, then gathered her into his arms, where she nestled as still as a wounded bird taken into hand. Through the shouting of his young daughters, who were grabbing at his trouser legs, my father could hear the soft shuddering of her sobs.

"I was sharing a room with Vogel, to save a few dollars," my father said when he understood why my mother had become so anxious, and this explanation stood unchallenged, then and down through the years of family lore.

"They said you checked out," my mother said weakly. "I was beside myself, I couldn't..."

"I did check out, of course," my father said. "I couldn't very well tell them at the front desk what I was doing. But I told them at the office. If you had phoned there, they could have told you."

"I didn't think."

"*I* didn't think, Bertie. I didn't think to let *you* know. It was Thursday, there were just a few days left and it didn't occur to me that you'd call." He paused. "Why *did* you call?" He stood back, holding my mother at arm's length.

"Oh..." A smile broke across my mother's tear-stained face, the slightly crooked smile that had softened my father's heart the first time they met and still had as firm a grip on him as it would continue to have for many years to come. "Oh, I completely forgot. We won, one of our jingles, Moishe's and mine. Third prize. A thousand dollars. I was so excited, I was calling to let you know."

"A thousand dollars!" Beyond that, my father was speechless, much to my mother's delight. He was a practical man and whatever doubts or disapprovals he had harboured about her time-consuming hobby seemed to vanish at the mention of that sum – not a possible or projected or dreamed of amount, but a reality, more than ten times the amount of his weekly salary. "You have the money?"

"Not yet. I had to write back and confirm that I was who I am and live at this address. They'll send a certified cheque by registered letter."

"That you are who you are..." my father echoed, still trying to absorb the news.

"And half of it is for Moishe, for the Cahans. You know that, Harry."

"Of course."

"They can really use it. Moishe was beside himself when he found out, and Rachel was in tears. They were here for dinner Friday night. That was when I phoned you..." Her smile faded but didn't disappear. "Then we were *both* in tears."

Of all the arguments, fights and crises my parents had in their long marriage, none was as happily ended as this one, what my mother would, years later, refer to as "the time your father disappeared and I made three hundred dollars."

"It should have been five hundred," my father would grumble.

Then they would always laugh, both of them, as if the two events had been causally linked, as if it had taken my father's disappearance to allow my mother to win the money, although, in fact, she had won the money before she knew of his disappearance, and wouldn't have known of his disappearance at all – he would not, in fact, have "disappeared" – had she not won the money and, as a result, tried to telephone him. The winning of the money, my father's safe return to her, to his family, to the tiny apartment in Coney Island, these were all remembered as a happy time, deliciously happy, if all too brief.

Moishe Cahan was a short, heavy-set man whose thick mat of hair on chest and shoulders startled me, a boy of five or six, years later when the Cahans visited us once in the summer and he took off his shirt; so thick was the hair on his chest, he seemed more apelike than human. My mother used to swear that he was a kind, gentle, humorous man when she first knew him, that Rachel had plucked herself a peach, but the man I knew was bitter, irritable, stern. I went from feeling apprehensive about him to strong dislike during that visit, when I saw him slap the face of one of his sons, Manny, a few years older than me, for not immediately coming when he was called. This change in his personality was the result of the bad hand the Depression had dealt him, my father said. It was because of that, I suppose, and my mother's deep affection for Rachel, that my parents didn't allow the disagreement over the division of the contest prize to ruin their friendship, although my father only barely concealed his distaste for the man and, after Rachel's death, communication between them and Moishe – his children long grown – trickled to an annual greeting card, then to nothing.

"I should get seven hundred dollars," Moishe said.

My mother, startled, didn't respond, but my father, for all his earlier disapproval and ridicule, was now an active participant in the venture. "Why is that, Cahan?" he snapped. They were at the Cahan apartment, which gave the other man a slight advantage. My father had brought a bottle of rye whisky along and the two men had already enjoyed a celebratory glass, complete with *l'chaim, mazel tov* and other toasts.

"Several reasons, Morgenstern. One, I discovered this particular contest. Berte, you'll bear me out?"

This was true, although my mother would surely have come across it too. The contest was advertised in both *Woman's Day* and *Family Circle*, magazines that both she and Rachel picked up for a nickel each where they did their shopping. That Moishe, who scoured the magazines the moment Rachel brought them home, had come across the ad first was only a testament to his idleness, not his greater zeal, but my mother didn't say that. She cast a glance at Rachel, who averted her own eyes.

"Two, I wrote the first line of the jingle."

"You wrote them together," my father protested. "All of them. I saw you with my own eyes."

"Yes, we did. I don't deny that. But every jingle, every poem, begins with a first line, and that is the most important line. Look at Shakespeare's sonnets – he didn't even title them, and we know them by their first lines. 'Shall I compare thee to a summer's day?' 'My mistress's eyes are nothing like the sun'..." Moishe's hands, which were hairy on the back but were unexpectedly small and well shaped, an architect's hands, flew excitedly about as he talked.

My father was an admirer of Shakespeare's sonnets, as Moishe well knew. "'When in disgrace with fortune and men's eyes,'" he shot back.

"Exactly," Moishe said, ignoring the sarcastic tone. "The first line sets the direction and tone of a poem. Isn't that right, Rachel?"

All eyes turned to Rachel now. She was a better poet than my mother, though not necessarily better than my mother might have been, had she worked at it harder, but she possessed the enviable cachet of having published some of her poems, not only in the literary magazine at Hunter College but in several of the small, mimeographed journals produced in Greenwich Village, where she and my mother had shared an apartment before their marriages. But Rachel didn't answer. She stood up abruptly and turned her back on her husband and her friends, going to stand beside the open living room window and stare stolidly down at the

Dave Margoshes

streetscape below, where women sat gossiping on stoops and children played on the sidewalk, their voices lifting gaily in the heavy summer air. Though it was still early evening, her own children were already in their beds, a rule of their strict father's, and my sisters were at home with a sitter.

"Well, it *is* right," Moishe persisted. "Don't you agree, Berte?"

"In a poem, yes," my mother said slowly.

"And in a jingle too. The first line sets the direction, the tone...everything. It isn't the jingle entire, but without it, the jingle cannot be."

"But Berte wrote the jingle *with* you," my father began again, marshalling his forces. "You wrote it together, like Rodgers and Hart. You think Rodgers gets more money because people come out of the theatre humming his music even though they can't remember the silly words Hart writes?"

"That's entirely different, Morgenstern. Without the words, there's no song, without the *music*, there's no song, they're equal partners. Here, we both wrote the jingle, yes, I don't deny that. I give full credit to Berte for her contribution, you know that, but *I* wrote the first line. Without that, the jingle couldn't have been what it became. We wouldn't have won."

"Third prize," my mother said quietly.

"If you'd used Bertie's first line, maybe you would have won *first* prize," my father said defiantly.

"Your darling wife didn't *write* a first line," Moishe said quickly. He thrust his chest out aggressively and clenched his fists. "*I* did, and we were away to the races. The jingle practically wrote itself. Isn't that right, Berte?" He didn't wait for an answer. "Listen, there were other times when Berte wrote the first line. If one of those had won, I'd be saying *she* should get a larger share."

My father threw up his hands and made a noise of exasperation. "Did you ever talk about these things? Bertie?"

But my mother wasn't listening to him. She'd gotten up and approached Rachel. She stood two or three feet behind her friend, gazing not *at* her, exactly, not over her shoulder, either, but at an indefinite point just above Rachel's shoulder. The two women stood motionless, two slender, dark-haired young women in similar light-coloured cotton skirts and sleeveless white blouses. My mother wore sandals; Rachel was barefooted. Rachel wore a tortoiseshell barrette in her hair, which was a coarse, crinkly black; my mother wore the blue velvet ribbon my father had given her in hers. Slanting evening sunlight streamed in through the window, illuminating their hair, their shoulders, their hands; my father couldn't see their faces. They stood so motionlessly that, when my father glanced at them, they appeared almost as if they were figures in a painting, perhaps by Monet, two women, sisters perhaps, perhaps lovers, certainly not rivals, caught in a moment of eternal time like flies enraptured by amber.

"Maybe you're right, Cahan," my father said after a long moment.

"I think he is," my mother said softly. She turned to gaze at her husband and there was on her face a look of such surprise and gratitude, an admixtured look such as he had never before seen, that it thrilled him to his bones. "Moishe wrote the first line."

"The first line *is* the most important," my father said. "And this one is a *good* first line. Not that I know anything about jingles. You two are the experts. But it's...catchy. It...catches..." His voice drifted off. My mother had turned back to Rachel, who hadn't moved, and this time she stepped closer, putting her hands

Dave Margoshes

lightly on her friend's arms, and my father found himself also engaged with hands – Moishe Cahan had
come across the room with his extended, and the two
men were shaking now, as if solemnizing an agreement.

"I knew you'd see it, Morgenstern," Moishe said.

When the cheque arrived, all four of them went to
the Cahans' bank and it was cashed and the money
divided according to the agreement reached that
evening, seven hundred to the Cahans, who, my mother
would say, "needed it much more than we did," three
hundred to my mother, who set it aside for my sisters'
college education. Afterwards, my father bought ice
cream cones for them all. The shopping certificate, by
agreement between my mother and Rachel, also went
to the Cahans, but both households wound up with
stainless steel pots and pans and other utensils, and
many of them were still in my mother's kitchen when
she died. My sisters and I shared them.

Though they all remained friends and continued to
see each other regularly – more so during the war, when
Moishe was overseas with the Signal Corps and Rachel
alone, less so after he returned and found a full-time job
– there were no more contests; despite their great success, my mother and Moishe seemed to have lost their
zeal for the competition. Actually, my father believed
that Moishe continued to enter contests on his own. But
if he ever won anything, my parents didn't hear of it.
Rachel Cahan continued to write poetry, some of which
was occasionally published. My mother continued to
write poems too, but they were read only by my father,
who had learned to read between their lines.

A Book of Great Worth

My father was there when the Hindenburg went down, killing thirty-six people.

Though labour was his specialty and he rarely covered regular news, he had been assigned, because of a staffing problem, to cover the dirigible's arrival in New Jersey, after its transatlantic flight from Germany. It was only his fourth day back at work after having been off for more than a week for an appendectomy and he was still sore, and after the long train ride to Lakehurst he was feeling quite a bit of discomfort. Gritting his teeth, he interviewed officials and some of the people in the large crowd that had come to watch, then found a chair where he could ease himself while he waited.

Ropes had been set up to keep the crowd at some distance, but that was more for the safety and convenience of the passengers than the sightseers, so he was no more than one hundred metres from where burning debris began to fall immediately after the explosion. Like everyone else there, my father was stunned by what happened. Heat blasted into his face as if he had opened the door to an oven and peered in to check the roast. His eyes flooded with tears, an automatic response of the body, he supposed, to protect them from the heat. Standing up to get a better view of the arrival in the moments just before the explosion, he was just a few steps from the radio man, chattering into his microphone, "Here it comes ladies and gentlemen, and what a sight it is, a thrilling one, a marvelous sight," then continuing to broadcast after the eruption of fire, which seemed, my father used to say when he told the story, literally to split the sky with dazzling colour, and, except in patches when bursts of explosion obliterated his voice, he could hear him clearly:

"It burst into flames, get out of the way, get out of the way, get this Johnny, get this Johnny, it's fire and it's flashing, flashing, it's flashing terribly...this is terrible, this is one of the worst catastrophes in the world...oh, the humanity and all the friends just screaming around here...I don't believe, I can't even talk to people whose friends are on there, it, it's, ah, I, I can't talk, ladies and gentlemen, honest it's a mass of smoking wreckage and everybody can hardly breathe and talk and screaming, lady, I, I'm sorry."

My father's account of that day – it was May 6, 1937 – became a favourite story, and my sisters and I and our cousins would often beg for a retelling. Everyone was running and, after a moment in which he was frozen in place, transfixed, my father was too, he said. His notebook and pen were in his hands and his mouth, he remembered, was open, and he ran, thinking not of his story or even of helping people – those in the dirigible or directly below it seemed beyond help, he said – but of his own safety, something which, when he would tell this story, years later, he conveyed without any discernible sense of shame but rather a small pride in his prudence. But when he had reached a safer distance and stopped to catch his breath and, scribbling in his pad in that illegible shorthand of his that used to fascinate me so much, begun to record the sights and sounds billowing in front of him like a film running haywire through a projector, only then did he feel the pain and wetness in his side and, holding open his suit jacket, see the spreading blossom of blood soaking his shirt.

His first thought was that he had been injured by a flying piece of debris, like the shrapnel or flak in the Great War he had heard so much about, but then he realized it was nothing that romantic or dangerous, that the stitches closing his incision had merely given way under stress and that, like a corroded bathroom fixture, he had begun to leak.

At that time, my father and mother were living in a small third-floor apartment in Coney Island with my two sisters; my birth was still four years away but my mother was pregnant with a child who, had he lived, would have been my brother or, perhaps, rendered my conception unnecessary. In addition to the four of them, there was a fifth person crammed into the small set of rooms: a living room with the apartment's one partial view of the ocean, jammed with an overstuffed sofa, upon which the guest slept, and two frayed easy chairs, rough bookshelves, a coffee table, lamps and my mother's piano, at which she instructed several wooden-fingered neighbourhood children; a kitchen so small that two people could barely stand at the sink to wash and dry the dishes; one small bedroom that was my parents'; and an even tinier room, not much bigger than a large closet but described as a den, in which my sisters slept, the eldest in a small bed, the younger on a folding cot permanently unfolded. This guest was a young woman my father had met several weeks earlier and invited home with him. She had come from Montreal in search of a man she described as her brother, a poet whom my father knew slightly. She had, on a slip of grimy, much-folded paper, the name and address of Fushgo's bookshop, through which the brother had told her he could always be reached. There, standing in one of the narrow aisles sandwiched in among the groaning walls of second-hand books my father loved to browse through, he'd met her.

"Morgenstern, I'm glad you stepped in," Fushgo said, beckoning him over. "A damsel in distress. Just the ticket, you are." He indicated the tiny woman standing beside the cash drawer so drably dressed and standing in so unimposing a posture that my father had at first failed to notice her. "This is Anna," Fushgo said, winking in the sly way he affected when he was trying to interest my father in a book beyond his means. "She is that rarest of women. She cannot speak."

My father was presented with a woman of indeterminate youthful age – she could have been sixteen, so smooth and clear was her skin, or thirty, so severe was the expression of her cloud-grey eyes – whose dirty yellow hair coiled like a tangle of unruly wool down the back of her tattered shawl, which at one time had been maroon. Everything about her was in disarray – the buttons of her white blouse askew, the hem of a slip showing beneath that of her pleated grey wool skirt, even the laces of her high shoes undone – but her clothing and hair, even the nails on the fingers of the small white hand she extended to my father, were clean, and she smelled of the sea, not the rank, oily waters of the East River that often shouldered its way on the back of fog along the Lower East Side, where he worked, or the flat, hotdoggy smell of the beach at Coney Island, but the bracing salt spray of the pounding surf at Far Rockaway, where he and my mother would sometimes go walking with the girls on Sunday afternoons. "Show, show," Fushgo grunted, prodding her with a sharp, tobacco-stained finger.

The woman offered my father a small sheet of paper obviously torn from a pad, and freshly so, judging by the clean, ragged edge, and already scribbled on with a sharp-pointed pencil. He took it from her, noticing that her delicately veined hand trembled. On the paper, in a handwriting that was both clear and immature, was written in a mixture of Yiddish and English: "My name is Anna Fishbine, from Montreal, in Canada. I am seeking my brother, Abraham Diamond, the poet, who receives his mail at this shop. Can you assist me?"

My father had several small weaknesses – *schnapps* and cigarettes among them – but only one great one, and that was his love of books, not merely reading them, a love which in itself could have been satisfied by the public library, but of possessing them, feeling their weight on his knee and the rough textures of their bindings on his fingers as he read, seeing the satisfying substance of them on the shelves he had constructed in the living room, the heavy dusty aroma wafting off their old, roughly cut pages as they lay open on the kitchen table. New books, with their crisp, clean jackets and unsoiled pages failed to impress him the way a book with a life and a history behind it did, so he was an addict to Fushgo's constantly replenishing stock and devoted to the man himself, his irritating mannerisms, come from a lifetime of communing with dead authors at the expense of living readers, notwithstanding. But my father, who had from time to time seen the poet at the Café Royale and had exchanged words with him on one or two occasions, had never encountered Diamond at the shop.

"Diamond gets his mail here?" my father asked, raising his eyes to Fushgo, who, despite his stoop, was a tall man.

"Only invisible letters," Fushgo said, raising his brows, "delivered by invisible mailmen."

The two men exchanged glances redolent of the

comfort that they felt in each other's presence. Both were shy men but they had a mutual love. They'd known each other for a dozen years and, over that time, my father had contributed to Fushgo's upkeep with the same regularity and consistency of a Christian tithing to his church. Fushgo shrugged his rounded shoulders, raggedly incised by the frayed stripes of his suspenders, and made a comical face with his eyes and blue-lipped mouth that suggested despair over the antics of women.

"How long since you heard from your brother?" my father asked.

At the woman's feet there was a brown cardboard suitcase. In her hands she clutched a blue leather purse from which she produced a pad and pencil, laying the purse awkwardly on the suitcase. She scribbled, looked up, scribbled again, then tore the page loose and handed it to my father.

"Six months without a word." Here was where she had hesitated. Then: "Our parents are frantic with worry."

My father nodded his head as he read. "Your brother often goes to the Café Royale. Do you know it?"

The woman shook her head, a look of mild fright briefly passing over her eyes.

"I'm on my way there now for a bite," my father said. "I'll escort you. It's a twenty-minute walk or so, can you manage?"

She nodded her head and smiled.

"Maybe you'll be lucky and he'll be there. Or someone will know where he might be found."

The woman seemed so grateful that my father was infused with a feeling of well-being that propelled them both out of Fushgo's shop onto East Broadway with the gentle force of a summer breeze. They turned north on Allen Street, passing Delancey and Houston, then over one block to Second Avenue and carried on for several blocks further north. It was early evening, the weather pleasant, and the streets were still crowded with people. One or two men they passed nodded at my father in recognition but if their faces betrayed surprise at seeing him with an unfamiliar young woman he didn't notice. My father carried Anna's suitcase, which seemed so light as to be almost empty, while she clutched her purse to her chest. Because of her silence – he didn't know at this point whether she was an actual mute or merely too frightened to speak – there was no need to chat, but my father grew expansive and rattled on, describing the scenery through which they passed and, occasionally forgetting, asking her questions she could not – or would not – answer without stopping to write on her pad. "That's all right," my father said. "Forget it." Or: "That was only a rhetorical question. There's no need to reply."

She paused several times, hindering their progress, to gaze into a shop window or down the length of a street they were crossing, and one of the rhetorical questions my father asked concerned the nature of Montreal, for the woman gave the appearance of having stepped directly from the boat or the country. He thought, for the first time in several years, of his unpleasant encounter with a cousin from that city almost a decade earlier and shook his head with distaste. He couldn't help but wonder if Abraham Diamond was a similar sort of charlatan.

At the Café Royale, there was no sign of Diamond nor any of the men whom my father thought he might have seen with the poet. Nevertheless, after he had placed the order – a corned beef sandwich with coleslaw and a pickle and coffee for him, strong tea for

Anna – he inquired of the waiter, who asked several others. Most didn't know Diamond but one who did said he hadn't seen him for several days. Perhaps this evening. Mendel and Solarterefsky, two playwrights my father knew, were at their usual table in a rear corner and he inquired of them as well. Both knew Diamond, and Mendel said he thought he'd seen him in the company of Ishavis Lazen, the actor, who was sure to be at the café that evening, after his performance in a play at the Second Avenue Theatre, just a few doors away. My father had a meeting to cover so he introduced Anna to the two men, spared her the effort of the notes by explaining her situation, entrusted her to their attention and left her there, promising to look in later. "Hopefully, you'll have found him, you'll be gone and happily ensconced in his apartment," he told her. "I'm sure all will be well."

My father went to his meeting, where he listened, took notes and afterwards talked to people in attendance. He went back to his office and sat at a heavy oak desk where he wrote an account of the meeting on a standard Royal machine with Yiddish characters. He and another man who was working late had a drink from a bottle of Canadian whisky my father kept in the lower drawer of his desk. He gave his story to Lubin, the assistant city editor, and he put on his raincoat before stepping out into the light drizzle that was falling in the darkness of East Broadway. He walked past Fushgo's shop, dark as an alley, and the Garden Cafeteria, closed but its lights still shining, and turned north towards the Café Royale, from which, as he approached, he could see light and hear noise spilling. Anna was sitting at the table where he had left her, an island of mute and painful isolation in the midst of the tables crowded with loud men. Mendel and Solarterefsky were gone, there was no sign of Lazen, though the theatres had let out more than an hour earlier and, as he'd feared, there was no sign of Diamond.

My father sat down and ordered a coffee. "I'm delighted to see you again, my dear," he said, "but sorry to find you alone. Was there no news?"

Anna wrote this note: "No. Mr. Mendel was most kind. He and the other gentleman introduced me to several men who know Abraham but no one has seen him for several weeks. There is a possibility he has a job with a touring company. Someone promised to inquire."

My father frowned and looked around the café, raising his hand to several men he knew. "Have you eaten?"

Anna nodded vigorously, but he was struck again by the emaciated quality to her small, smooth face that he found so appealing, the cheekbones high, the skin tight and without lines except for the sheerest hint beside her nose where, though he had yet to see her display the ability, surely she must occasionally smile.

"Are you sure? The cheesecake here is very good. I wouldn't mind one myself but I couldn't manage the whole thing. Would you help me?"

She agreed and, when it came, ate all but the few forkfuls my father took to put her at ease.

She looked down at the plate, as if ashamed at the weakness her hunger had revealed.

"You have a room?" my father asked. "Someplace where you're staying? Perhaps I should take you there."

Anna looked up, then down again. On her pad she wrote: "I had hoped I would find Abraham."

"So you have no place?"

She shook her head and they sat in silence while my father smoked a cigarette and finished his coffee. "I want you to understand," he said presently, "that I'm a married man, with two wonderful children and a third on the way. So please don't construe my intentions as anything but the most honourable."

Anna wrote: "Surely your wife will object."

My father smiled. "Bertie would never turn someone away from her door."

Again he carried the suitcase, extending the elbow of his other arm to her on the dark street and, after a moment's hesitation, she took it. On the long subway ride home he wondered if what he'd said was true, but my mother, of course, would be asleep, and if she did object, he knew, it wouldn't be until afterwards. Not once, as the subway car lurched through its velvety tunnels or as he made up the bed for her on the sofa in the tiny living room, did he question his motives, not once did he long to heal her wounded tongue with his own.

My mother did have a generous heart, and patience that, after three weeks, was beginning to grow thin. She was four months pregnant and suffering greatly, her body wracked by cramps at all times and swept by waves of dizziness and nausea when she moved with anything but the most deliberate slowness. False calms would arise during which it appeared the worst was over, then the pain and sickness would come crashing back without warning. Inside her, the baby seemed to be warring with the notion of its own life. There was no question but that Anna could be useful. My oldest sister, Esther, was almost six and already in school, but the younger one, Judy, was only three and needed care and attention, and diversion during my mother's worst times. My father, who always worked into the evenings and often later, saw to the children in the mornings,

Dave Margoshes

getting the eldest off to school, while my mother stayed in bed preparing herself for the day ahead, but in the afternoons, after he'd gone, the little one often grated on her nerves, Esther was soon home demanding to be heard and there was a meal to prepare, then bathing. As the pregnancy deepened and the nature of the ailment became clearer, a plan had taken shape to have my mother's younger sister Sarah join the household to help her; Anna's presence made that unnecessary. She immediately took charge; at the same time, her presence grated on my mother, aggravating her already stripped nerves. By day, Anna helped in the apartment, relieving my father of some of his morning duties, but, more importantly, being there in the afternoon, playing with the younger one, keeping her quiet and amused while my mother lay propped up against pillows on her bed reading detective novels and feeling the muscles in her legs slowly turn to jelly. Sometimes, rising to go to the bathroom, my mother would open the bedroom door and find Anna and my sister sitting side by side on the piano bench, the little girl enthralled as Anna's fingers silently raced over the keys my mother hadn't touched in weeks, just above them, producing a music only the two of them could hear.

In the evenings, the guest took the subway to Manhattan and the Café Royale where, like an urchin awaiting her drunken father, she sat at a table by herself and passed notes to people asking: "Have you seen Abraham Diamond?" My father often dropped in on her there and, if his work kept him late, would stop at the café on his way home to give her company on the long subway ride, which still frightened her.

My mother, without accusing him of anything, clearly resented the attention he paid to the girl. "Three weeks and still no sign of that *brother*," she said on a

Saturday. Anna had taken the girls for a stroll on the boardwalk and she and my father were alone at the breakfast table.

My father shrugged. "It appears he's gone with a company on a road trip. No one seems to know for sure where they are or when they'll be back. What do you mean *brother*?"

"Oh, Harry, it's as clear as the nose on your face that the man is her husband. Or her lover. God knows if there really are worried parents in Montreal. The woman has been *abandoned*."

"You really think so?"

My mother rolled her eyes upward, as if to seek support from the angel of the ceiling. "Men are so blind."

"If you're right, all the more reason to give her sympathy and support," my father said after a moment.

"You think so?" my mother said sharply.

At times like these my father would often retreat to his books, forming his own private library wherever he was sitting, the world shut out by an invisible, soundproof barrier as he pored over the pages of his latest acquisition. Although he had gone no further in school than the fifth grade before he'd been required to begin to help support his family, and English was his third language, after Yiddish and Polish, he was partial to Shakespeare and – inexplicably – the American Civil War, but his deepest passion was for the classics, and his most treasured possession was a richly illustrated edition of Caesar's *Wars* in Latin that he had taught himself to read. He had paid Fushgo ten dollars for the Caesar, more than four times the portion of his weekly allowance that he allotted to himself for books and, with the interest Fushgo charged, it had taken more than a month for him to pay it off. In later years, he would acquire huge volumes of Dante rich with Blake engravings, and, though he wasn't at all religious, a variety of Bibles, in several languages, their oiled leather bindings giving off a smoky aroma of history, damnation and salvation. At this particular time, he was engrossed in a book that appeared to have been handwritten, in the manner of monks, in a language he had not been able to identify. The handwriting was skillful and consistent throughout the several hundred pages, the unintelligible words clearly scripted in a faded blue ink, the enlarged capitals at the beginning of each new paragraph shadowed in a red the shade of dried blood. There was no date, no publisher's name or city, no illustrations that might serve as clues to the book's origin, and the title and author were just as indecipherable as the text itself. The leather of the binding was so thick – more like a slab of oxblood hide used for making shoes than the soft black grainy cloth publishers used – and the spine so warped the book could not be fully closed, and when it lay on a table it seemed like a head whose jaws had sprung open, eager to share the untapped wisdom within it. "For you, Morgenstern," Fushgo had said when he produced the book for my father. "Read this and you'll learn much the same wisdom you acquire conversing with your Anna." And he laughed, Fushgo, spraying the dark air of his shop with tobacco-scented breath.

For hours at a time my father would sit poring over the book, comparing the strange script with works from his collection in Latin, Greek, Russian, Hebrew, not that he thought this language could be any of those but hoping for some clue, some similarity of characters that would provide a hook, an opening through which he might shoulder to some dim understanding of the message the old pages indifferently held. One night when he had come home early he was sitting at the kitchen table engrossed in the magic letters, my mother asleep in their room, when Anna came home from the café, her small shoulders rising in their inevitable shrug to my father's raised eyes. She came and sat beside him and he poured them both glasses of the cheap port he favoured for drinking at home. She sipped hers, then wrote this note: "I fear I may never find Abraham."

"Surely not," my father said. Then, after a long silence: "But you should give some thought to what you'll do, just in case. Have you written to your parents?"

Anna hesitated, then wrote: "Neither can read."

"And the neighbours? A friend or *landsman* who could read a letter to them."

Anna shook her head. "There is only me," she wrote. "I must return to them soon."

My father nodded. "You know you're welcome to stay here as long as you want. Bertie is irritable, I know, but it's the baby, not you." He put his hand on hers, marvelling at its smallness, the way her entire hand, even the slender fingers, disappeared beneath the cup of his palm.

Anna smiled and wrote: "You're very kind."

She gestured towards the book and my father slid it to her. "This is a book of great worth," he said.

She bent over it, puzzled, then raised her head, her cheeks and mouth and eyes molded into a quizzical smile of such sweetness that it pierced my father like an arrow fashioned of the finest, purest gold.

"Eskimo?" she wrote.

As my father's one indulgence was his books, my mother's was her piano. It was an upright Baldwin of indeterminate age, the ivory of its keys yellowed like Fushgo's ancient teeth. It had been purchased at a second-hand shop on the Bowery with one hundred dollars it took her three years to save and had been lifted by rope and tackle along the outside wall of the building and brought into the apartment through a window. My mother had studied the piano as a child and music for two years at college. She'd long since given up any ambitions of the concert stage, but her greatest delight was to sit at the piano in the evening, the music students of the afternoon just an unpleasant taste in her mouth, the children in bed and my father not yet home from work or, perhaps, enveloped in one of the overstuffed chairs reading, one ear cocked, and play the concerti and sonatas of Mozart, which were her passion, and Chopin, which my father preferred. Since the third month of the pregnancy, the lessons had been cancelled and my mother, her head light, stomach lurching, legs and fingers aching, had sat not once at the piano, and the apartment resonated in the evening with a silence that seemed more like a presence than an absence.

Into this silence, where one would have thought she would be comfortable, Anna intruded, passing this note to my mother one evening: "When you are out and I won't disturb you, may I play the piano?"

"Of course," my mother said with irritation. She rarely left the apartment but when she did she could care less what happened in her absence. "You play?"

Anna nodded, smiling shyly.

"Let me hear."

"Won't your head hurt?" Anna wrote.

"My head's fine today. I'd play myself but my fingers have rubber bands around them."

Anna sat at the bench and raised the cover, exposing the Baldwin's soiled smile. She raised her chin, facing the window that looked out – past the roof of the hat factory across the street – at the ocean, stretching with calm indifference towards the horizon and the old world beyond it. After a moment, she began to play. Chopin. The Fifth Concerto. My father, who had been in the bathroom shaving, came to the door with a broad smile on his lathered face, saying "That's wonderful, Bertie," then filled the doorway in confusion, looking from my mother, who stood by the window, to Anna at the piano and back again.

"I'm sorry, my head *is* hurting," my mother said after a while.

My father's appendicitis attack came completely without warning. At dinnertime, he had a sandwich, salad, coffee and piece of cheese Danish at the Garden Cafeteria, then went for a short walk to allow the food to settle before stopping at Fushgo's for a chat and a drink from the bottle the bookseller kept behind his counter. He began to feel ill immediately after downing the shot, and Fushgo had to help him back to the newspaper office where he sat at his desk taking deep gasps, his face drained of all colour, until the ambulance arrived. My mother was telephoned from the hospital and she came at once, leaving the children with Anna, who had been just about to leave for her nightly visit to the Café Royale. The appendix was removed that night and when my father awoke from the ether the next morning, my mother was sitting on a straight chair beside his bed, his hand in hers. She'd been there all night and her face was etched with pain and exhaustion.

"Who's the patient?" my father said. "I should get up, you should get into this bed, the way you look. Or better yet, we should both be in it. The way you look." He squeezed her hand.

"It's too narrow," my mother said, smiling.

"Too narrow?" my father said. "According to who?"

She told him what the doctors had said. He asked for a cigarette and she told him they were forbidden. He told her about the drink he'd had with Fushgo. "It's the first time liquor's ever hurt me," he said. They laughed and gazed at each other fondly.

"Anna's with the children?" he asked after a while.

"Yes."

"Thank God we have her. Especially now."

My mother didn't say anything right away. Then: "She'll be a great help while you're here, yes. But when you're home I'd like to have Sarah come."

My father was silent.

"It's been over a month. We can't be responsible for the woman forever. She's taking advantage of your kindness."

My father nodded slowly. "After I'm home," he said.

He was in hospital for four days and was under strict orders to rest and not go back to work for a week after he went home. The attack had come on a Friday and he was released on the following Tuesday. By the doctor's orders, he shouldn't have gone back to work until the following Wednesday, but the city editor phoned and he went on the Monday. He felt fine, if a little tired, the incision, already beginning to scar over with bright pink flesh shiny as fingernails, just a little tender. On Thursday afternoon, feeling completely fit, he went by train to Lakehurst, not thinking a thing of it.

It was well after midnight when he came home, my mother asleep, the living room dark. He'd served his editor as well as he could, though he'd retreated from the scene soon after he began to bleed and was unable to attract the attention of any of the medical people who rushed to the airfield. In the town itself, he found a small hospital already beginning to be overwhelmed by the flood of injured from the accident site, and, while he was waiting, telephoned in his story. After several hours, a nurse whose hair had slipped out of its careful bun into shreds of haphazard grey cleaned his wound of the coagulated blood crusting it and bound him securely in bandages wrapped around his lower chest and belly. No doctor was available, though, so no stitches were taken, and it was this delay – the opening required seven stitches the following day, when he reported to the hospital where he'd originally been treated – that caused the odd shape and thickness of the scar he carried the rest of his life.

My father went to the kitchen and poured himself a whisky from the flask he kept in his raincoat pocket, drank it quickly and poured another. The ceiling light spilled through the doorway into the living room and he could see there was no one sleeping on the sofa. He went into the bedroom and sat down heavily on the bed and took off his shoes. My mother, who had been sleeping lightly, rolled over and opened her eyes, reaching out her hand to touch his arm.

"Harry? What time is it?"

"Almost one. Go back to sleep." He bent over her and kissed her head.

"How was it?"

"You didn't hear?"

"No, I didn't play the radio."

"I'll tell you in the morning."

"Okay." She rolled over.

"Anna's not back from the cafe?" my father asked.

"She's gone."

"I thought not till next week."

"We had an argument," my mother said. "I asked her to go."

"I see," my father said. He tried to imagine what

such an argument would have been like, the flurry of notes being scribbled, torn from the pad, crumpled, thrown to the floor.

"I'll tell you in the morning. Sarah's coming in the evening."

He took off his shirt and went out of the room, closing the door quietly behind him. He stepped into the small room where my sisters slept and gazed down at them, muffled in darkness but glowing haloes around their heads formed by the street light from the window drawn to their hair. He bent over each head and kissed it. In the kitchen, he slowly drank the whisky he'd poured. A dull red stain the size and shape of a strawberry had gathered on the bandage just below and to the right of where, he believed, his heart lay. His body was exhausted but his mind raced, filled with the dazzle of flame, its surprisingly loud roar, the plaintive voice of the radio man, "get out of the way, get out of the way, get this Johnny, get this Johnny." He walked across the living room to the shelf and found the book written in the mysterious language and took it back to the kitchen. He sat at the table, the open book in front of him, and looked first at its inscrutable script, then up at the icebox, standing silent and white against the wall. From the living room, he thought he heard the tinkling of piano keys, the first tentative notes of a Chopin concerto, but it was only the sound of an automobile passing on the street below, rising through the warm night air and the open window. His side ached, just beneath the strawberry stain by his heart, and he didn't know if it was the incision, or something else.

The Barking Dog

The war in Europe began; the Depression ended. Really, it was almost like that. At *The Day*, where my father had been a reporter for fifteen years, there was unrest. The paper had kept its head above water all through the bad years but salaries were frozen. The staff was lucky to have jobs, lucky to have salaries as high as they'd been before the Crash – my father made seventy dollars a week, which was a fine income compared to many others. But now, after ten years, the journalists wanted more. The war hadn't really begun, but everyone could see it coming. The Depression wasn't really over, but there were signs it would be. Some of my father's colleagues were reasonable, others were more demanding; the union leaders were mostly Communists and, my father said, were glad to have a chance. Fascists must be fought, at home as well as abroad. Before my father knew it, it was spring and he was on strike.

It couldn't have come at a worse time. Through most of the Thirties, my parents and their young family – my two sisters – had lived in a cramped apartment in Coney Island, saving their pennies. Just the year before, they had finally realized their dream: they'd bought a small piece of land in New Jersey, on a country road not far from Princeton, and, using plans drawn by their friend Moishe Cahan, who had left architecture school after the Crash to work as a draftsman, supervised the construction of a house, a dream house with three bedrooms, a kitchen bathed in light and a stone fireplace. In late January 1939, two months before my father went on strike, they'd moved all their belongings into the new house and he became a commuter, riding in the smoking car of a rattling New Jersey Central local train mornings from Princeton Junction to lower Manhattan, and back again in the evening. Now he was taking the train every morning to walk on a picket line. There was a mortgage as big as Yankee Stadium and, in addition to my mother and two small children, two goats, two ducks, a dog and a cat to feed. Strike pay was ten dollars a week.

To make matters worse, my mother had just learned she was pregnant again.

Every penny they'd saved had been sunk into the house, so there was no cushion. Most of their relatives, on both my father's side and my mother's, and friends had fared more poorly than them during the Depression years, so there was no one to borrow from.

"We could sell Esther," my father said, straight-faced.

"NO!" my sister shrieked. She had turned eight just a week earlier.

"Ah, who would buy her anyway." And my father grabbed her and smothered her with tickles. "We'll sell Judy instead."

"NO!" Now my other sister was adding to the bedlam.

"You're right, too small. No good for anything... except...tickling..."

"It's no laughing matter, Harry," my mother scolded.

"That's why I'm laughing."

They both laughed at that, ruefully, but it was one of the last times for a long time that they'd find anything funny.

Years earlier, before my father had begun to write and followed his father and oldest brother into the newspaper trade, he had worked as a silversmith. Another older brother, Nathan, had already entered that trade and was doing well at it – eventually, he would have a job fashioning silver handles for canes and expensive umbrellas at a company in Lancaster, Pennsylvania, would rise to be a foreman, then a manager, and wind up buying the company and becoming rich. But at the time my father, just nineteen or twenty, was looking for a job, Nathan was employed at the firm of Tiffany and Co., makers of fine lamps. He recommended my father, and he was hired as an apprentice. In all, my father worked there for two or three years, first doing the smallest and simplest of jobs, later graduating to more complex handiwork. He enjoyed the work, but at night he would scribble stories and poems on sheets of scrap newsprint from the newspaper where his father was the editor, and dream of being a writer.

Now, twenty-five years later, my father put his hat in his hands and went to the Tiffany shop on Delancey Street to beg for a job.

No one then working at Tiffany's had been there in my father's day, and there were no open jobs there at any rate, but someone suggested he try Goldmans', down the street. There, he found, to his surprise, that a man named Arthur Reubens, who'd worked by his side at Tiffany's years before, was the foreman. Reubens, like my father, was an admirer of rare old books, and over the years the two had occasionally run into each other at Fushgo's bookshop on East Broadway.

"So you've given up on that crazy idea of being a writer, Morgenstern," Reubens remarked dryly when my father walked into the shop, as if it had been only weeks since he'd left the trade, not years.

"Right now it's given up on me," my father said. Everyone knew about the strike at *The Day*, now in its third week, and everyone on the Lower East Side knew my father, who wrote a popular column, worked there, so there was no need to explain.

The two men shared a laugh and shook hands warmly. Reubens offered my father a job on the spot and had him working the very next day. My father wasn't clear whether there really had been an opening or if Reubens, out of kindness, had created one.

Goldmans' was an old establishment with a reputation. It had been founded before the turn of the century by two brothers who'd worked as skilled craftsmen in Berlin and they quickly developed a demand for their fine tableware, candlesticks, menorahs and decorative pieces, in both silver and gold. The original Goldman brothers were dead now, and even their sons, Gerson and Sidney, were nearing retirement age. They made appearances every day, but mostly confined themselves to the front office, to buying supplies and marketing to the Fifth Avenue shops that carried their wares. They left the actual running of the workshop to the much-trusted Reubens.

There were a dozen men in the shop, of various nationalities, "a regular League of Nations," my father told my mother appreciatively. "The Goldmans don't care who you are as long as you can do the work." Among the men was Shel Goldman, Gerson's son, who was just learning the trade. In a few years, the business would belong to him, as Sid had never married, but for the moment he was just another hand in the shop, doing what Reubens told him to do.

On my father's first morning at work, Shel Goldman came over to say hello and my father was impressed by the young man's good nature. "Welcome to the sweatshop," he said with a wink, offering his hand. As *The Day*'s labour reporter, my father had written countless articles about the sweatshops of the garment district and the struggle by the unions against them. "You got tired of covering strikes and decided to see them from the inside out?" Goldman asked amiably.

"Of strikes I've seen plenty," my father said. "But what can you do?"

Perhaps inevitably, there was also a man who took an instant dislike to my father. This was Pat Callahan, a big, redheaded goldsmith of such high skill that his eccentricities, irascibility and barely concealed anti-Semitism were tolerated. When they were introduced, Callahan took one look at my father's soft white hands and new dungarees, snorted in disgust and turned back to his bench without a word. My father was flabbergasted.

"Pay no attention to Paddy," Reubens said with a shrug, just loud enough so that Callahan could hear. "He's the resident grouch." Some of the other men laughed but my father felt uneasy. Callahan was lighting his torch and, with that in his hand and in his leather apron, he looked formidable. Not a good man to get on the wrong side of.

Over the next few days, my father learned to stay out of Callahan's way. He was, Reubens assured him, more bark than bite. But still, the foreman added, "Who needs a barking dog at your heels?" The evening before, after work but before catching his train home, my father had spent an hour on the picket line at *The Day*, and there was a heckling group of men from the Bund across the street, in black leather jackets like German storm troopers. One of them had a snarling police dog on a short leash and the memory made my father shiver.

Reubens put my father to work on candlesticks and menorahs. Other, more skilled men made the parts, and my father's job was limited to welding pieces together and final polishing. He was given a bench next to Shel Goldman's; he was doing similar work. It was natural, then, that my father got to know the younger man better, and he took a liking to him. My mother would pack a lunch for my father, two peanut butter and jelly sandwiches on thick-sliced pumpernickel bread, a wedge of cheese and an apple, and a Thermos of coffee, which my father liked milky and sweet. Lunch breaks at the shop were staggered and, invariably, when he took his break, Goldman was going off on his as well and the two men would find themselves eating together in a small windowless room at the rear of the business office that served as a lunchroom. The two women who worked in the front, looking after correspondence and the books, had done what they could to prettify the lunchroom, tacking pages from a Currier and Ives calendar on the walls and arranging gingham placemats on the wobbly tables.

"In the old days," my father remembered, looking around on the first day, "when Reubens and I worked at Tiffany's, we'd walk down to Orchard Street and have the free lunch at Stinky's."

"Free!" Goldman said, impressed.

"Well, you bought a schooner of beer, three cents, then you helped yourself. Trays of black bread, sliced meat and cheese, pickles."

"First the beer, though."

"Sure, first the beer."

"And at inflated prices, I'm sure."

"I suppose. You could get the same glass of beer for two cents some places."

"So there's no free lunch. That it, Morgenstern?"

My father smiled. He thought about how the free kisses my mother had lavished on him had led to the diaper bucket, the mortgage, lunch in a paper bag. "No free lunch, Goldman. You're right about that."

Shel Goldman was a thin, ascetic-looking man with the hands of a concert pianist or a jeweller – not a metal smith – and dark, haunted eyes that made my father wonder if he was recovering from a tragic love affair. It wasn't the sort of thing you could ask another man about, but it wasn't long before my father found out.

As it turned out, Shel Goldman was a poet and, as soon as he felt sufficiently comfortable with my father, he was pressing some of his work into the older man's hands. By this time, a few weeks into my father's employment at Goldmans', the two men were eating their sandwiches together daily and had come to enjoy each other's company.

In his own younger days, my father had written poems and two novels, which had been serialized in the Cleveland newspaper where he'd worked. But he felt his literary days were behind him. At *The Day*, he wrote news stories and articles every day and a weekly column that had a large following; that seemed to satisfy his writerly impulses. As for literature, he explained, he read novels now, didn't write them. And it was a long time since he'd even read a poem, other than my mother's, let alone written one.

"Just wait till you have children," he told Goldman with a laugh. "Art goes out the window." But he cheerfully accepted the younger man's handwritten pages and read them with interest on the train ride home to Princeton Junction that evening.

My father would always willingly admit that he'd never been much of a poet. He was self-taught, having consumed Shakespeare, Wordsworth, Whitman, Emily Dickinson and Rilke, whom he considered gods, and he had a well-earned command of the written word, at least in Yiddish. But he had a tendency to go on and on that had seemed more suitable to novels. Goldman's poems, though, were short and pithy, filled with vivid images and startling metaphors that had my father shaking his head with admiration. They were love poems, written in English, and they expressed a painful longing for a departed lover, a beautiful, enigmatic woman, sensuously described, who, if the poems were to be believed, had spurned all emotional advances while encouraging physical contact, allowing herself to be both available and distant. "That's one mystery solved," my father thought.

That night, after the girls had been put to bed, he showed a few of Goldman's poems to my mother, who was also a lover of poetry. At college, she'd read Verlaine and Rimbaud in French and had written some poems, and continued to write occasionally, though she considered herself no more than an amateur. "He's good," she agreed. "Too good to be wasting himself in a metal shop. You should encourage him."

"He's the boss's son," my father reminded her.

"I don't understand," my mother said.

"What if I tell him to quit, go to university, live in a garret and drink wine? His father will be sore at me. What if I tell him to write poetry on weekends, keep his nose clean and learn the business? He may think I don't take him seriously and resent it. Giving advice can come back and bite you on the behind."

Giving advice happened to be something my father knew about. Years earlier, in Cleveland, he had written an advice to the lovelorn column, questions as well as answers at first, which still embarrassed him to admit. On more than one occasion, advice he gave had produced results that were far less than satisfactory.

"How do you know he wants your advice?" my mother asked.

"Why else show me the poems?"

"Maybe he just wants to hear what you think of *them*," she said, drawing a fine distinction.

"Maybe," my father said, without much conviction.

"But you said he's such a nice young man," my mother protested after a minute of thought.

"Nice, yes. The boss's son, also yes."

The next day, it was fine outside and my father suggested to Goldman that they take their brown bags to the little park a few blocks away on Delancey and eat on a bench. They ate their sandwiches, commented on the burgeoning foliage of spring and the passersby and enjoyed the sunshine on their faces. Goldman seemed anxious but didn't press. "That must have been some love affair," my father finally said, choosing his words carefully. "She must have been some woman."

"Pardon?"

"The poems."

"Oh." Goldman blushed and looked away. "Poetic licence," he said after a moment.

My father looked at him, not at all certain what he was driving at. "You mean..."

"I'm a homosexual, Morgenstern," Goldman blurted out. "Do you know what I mean?"

"Of course." My father glanced at his young friend, then away. He'd heard of such people, of course, read about them, but had never met one, not that he knew of. He had no idea what they might do, what they might feel.

They'd finished their lunches and now they got up and began to stroll through the park, my father taking the lead. "Maybe poetry's not the best way to write of such things," he offered.

"It fooled you, didn't it?"

"Yes, but it...it made me ask you..."

"But I didn't have to tell you. I could have hidden behind the images of the poems. The poems stand on their own, speak for themselves. Maybe poetry's exactly the right way to write of such things, Morgenstern."

"If writing about such things is required," my father said. They'd come to the end of the small park and they turned around.

"And isn't it?" Shel Goldman asked.

"Ah," my father said. "That's the question."

So engrossed were they in conversation that they returned to the shop a few minutes late. Reubens gave them a sharp glance as they took their places at their benches and my father knew that, had he been on his own or with any of the other men in the shop, the foreman would have come over with a cutting word. Friendship, a shared history, a shared love of old books, none of that mattered on the shop floor. He saw that Callahan had also noticed the late return. He sat glowering at his bench, directly across the shop from my father's, hurling scowls in my father's direction like burning spears. But it was none of the Irishman's business, and my father merely shook his head and got quickly to work.

Over the next few weeks, as the weather turned from mild to balmy, my father and Shel Goldman took many lunches in the park and walks, although they were careful not to return late again. My father and the younger man, each with his own problems, became friends, though how close my father couldn't say.

On one of their early walks, Goldman's hand brushed against my father's sleeve and my father's arm involuntarily jerked.

"You have nothing to fear from me, Morgenstern," Goldman said.

"My dear Goldman, I didn't think I had."

"I thought perhaps you..." the younger man began.

"Certainly not. That was the farthest thought from my mind."

"I can assure you, Morgenstern..."

"Don't say another word, Goldman."

And without giving it any thought, my father extended his own right hand and the two men shook warmly. After that, while engaged in conversation, my father would often lightly touch the younger man on the arm or shoulder as a deliberate gesture of friendship.

Often on these lunch-break walks, Goldman would show my father a new poem. Like the first batch he'd seen, they were short, vivid love poems, but my father read them in a new light, with new understanding.

"This is deep," he offered after reading one such poem that moved him. Up till then, he had successfully avoided making comments that implied any judgment other than generalized approval.

Now, Goldman looked up with frank appreciation on his face. "Thank you, Morgenstern," he said.

"Have you...considered publication?" my father ventured.

"No," Goldman said quickly. "No, I couldn't. You know, I haven't even shown them to anyone other than you."

"I'm flattered."

"Please don't take this the wrong way, Morgenstern. It's hard to talk to people about certain things. My father, my family, would be horrified if they knew. But you...I saw in you, right from the first day, a man with an open mind."

"Now I'm doubly flattered." My father laughed with pleasure. "I hope I haven't disappointed you."

"No, not at all."

They walked in silence, heading back towards the shop, both of them suddenly conscious of the time.

They reached the door and paused. "Do you really think they might be suitable for publication?" Goldman asked.

My father smiled ruefully. "I'm afraid I'm not the man to ask that, Goldman. What I know about such things you could put in a candle holder."

Later that same afternoon, as my father was lingering in the men's room for a few puffs of a cigarette, Callahan came in. "Ah, I would have expected to find you in here with your sweetheart," the goldsmith spat.

"I beg your pardon?" my father said.

"The Goldman boy. Aren't you two special friends?"

My father was so astounded he could think of nothing to say. He shook his head in disgust, stubbed out his cigarette and went back to work. He was surprised, first of all, that Callahan knew or even suspected Goldman's secret, which he, my father, would never have guessed himself; and amazed that the Irishman had linked the two of them, though whether he really believed it or was merely being mischievous my father couldn't know.

Now he had three problems, he explained to my mother that evening. He had already told her, as delicately as he could, what Goldman had revealed to him, and was somewhat surprised that she knew what the term referred to. My mother, who had attended Hunter College for two years, was constantly surprising my father.

"Now I have the question of his poetry to be careful about, this other matter, even more inflammatory, and on top of it all, this Nazi Irishman," he said.

My mother shook her head in sympathy. All she had to worry about were looking after the two girls, preparing meals for them all and her pregnancy, which was then in the morning-sickness phase.

"Did he ask for advice about the poems? Young Mr. Goldman?" she asked.

"Not really" my father admitted. "Neither about writing poetry nor about the poems themselves. But about whether to seek publication."

"And you told him?"

"What could I tell him other than what do I know of such things?"

"And has he asked advice about...the other matter?"

"Certainly not."

"Well..." My mother smiled. "You *are* an authority on matters of the heart."

He laughed. "No, I don't think Shel Goldman will seek the counsel of Yenta Schmegge." That was the name under which my father had written the advice column years before.

"And as for the Irishman," my mother said, "don't let him provoke you, Harry."

"This you don't need to tell me, Bertie," my father said.

But the very next morning, the goldsmith did provoke my father.

"You like strikes so much, why ain't you over there walking on the picket line with your Red friends?" he asked as my father passed by his bench.

My father, who was usually the most mild-mannered

of men, replied with a comment he immediately regretted.

Callahan dropped his tools and bounded around his bench with a surprising agility and speed. "What in thunder..." my father began, but before he could say more Callahan's head butted into his chest. The goldsmith was a short, stocky man, and the force of his assault sent my father's glasses flying and my father himself to the floor, where he lay for a moment, dazed. Then the Irishman began to kick him.

This roused my father, who grabbed Callahan's legs and pulled. The goldsmith fell to the shop floor in a clatter. Then the two men were on their knees, trading blows. My father was taller but lighter than his adversary, but he was surprisingly strong and he held his own. But before either man could inflict much damage, the other men in the shop were clambering around them and burly arms pulled them apart.

"Enough!" Reubens commanded. Callahan and my father staggered to their feet but were restrained from moving towards each other. My father was conscious of Goldman's hands on his arms. The foreman looked first at one man, then the other. "Good, both of you have drawn blood. So it's a draw."

Goldman handed my father his glasses and he put them on. Indeed, he could see a trickle of blood coming from Callahan's nose, which produced in him a surprising feeling of satisfaction, and when he gingerly touched his lip his fingers came away wet and red.

Reubens continued to glower at the two men, and my father was sure he'd be fired. But the foreman only shook his head. "Jackasses! You think this is Kaplan's Gym? Get back to work."

Everyone returned slowly to their benches. My father took up his welding torch but, before he even had it lit he laid it down again and went into the bathroom. He was washing his face in the grimy sink when he heard footsteps and his head jerked up. "It's just me, Morgenstern."

My father dried his face with a paper towel. "Nice bunch you have working here, Goldman," he said. His lip winced with pain as he smiled.

"That was about me, wasn't it, Morgenstern?"

"You? No. No. What makes you say that?"

The younger man didn't reply. The two men looked at each other. After a moment, Goldman stepped into the stall and tore off a length of toilet paper. He carefully folded it in half, then quarters, then eighths. "Hold still, Morgenstern." He came close, raised his hand and, with surprising delicacy, patted a drop of blood from my father's lip. He smiled weakly, as if it were *his* lip that was bruised. "A mark of honour," he said.

My father shook his head. "There's no honour in blood, Shel."

At lunchtime, the two men took their paper bags as usual and walked in silence to the park. They ate their sandwiches in silence. My father gazed at the blue, cloudless sky, at the bright green canopy of leaves of the oak trees that lined the path. He listened to the honking of horns and the rumble of taxis on Delancey Street. He waited for Goldman to speak again. Eventually, though, he took the lead.

"For God's sake, Goldman, the poems, publish them. Write more. Think of yourself."

The strike at *The Day* dragged on through the summer and into the fall, then through the winter. It appeared it would never end. The war in Europe worsened and a pall of gloom hung over the Lower East Side. My father moved on from Goldmans' to a smaller shop where he was given more difficult tasks and the pay was commensurately better. His young friend had already left, "to pursue his star," my father used to say. He moved to the West Coast and my father never heard from him again. In the seventh month of her pregnancy, my mother miscarried. The dead child was the boy she badly wanted. His sacrifice, like that of another miscarried baby a few years earlier, made my own life possible because, a few months after the strike abruptly was settled, my mother became pregnant yet again. My father and his colleagues at *The Day* were betrayed by the Communists who led them and went back to work at notably lower wages, but considered themselves lucky to be back behind their desks. Slowly, over the next few years, as the United States entered the war and the economy boomed, the bosses relented and wages rose to the level they'd been at before the strike, and even above that, but long before that my parents had lost their dream house.

The Family Circle

When my father's cousin Glicka was a young woman of nineteen, she met a man from somewhere in Canada and went to live with him, somewhere far in the west and north where Eskimos ate whale blubber in round ice houses and the sun never set. That was the family story, at any rate. "How can you sleep in a place like that?" my uncle Henry, who had a philosophical bent, would ask whenever the subject came up, though it rarely did. She died in her third childbirth, we'd heard, and her memory receded, but my father, who I believe had been sweet on her as a child, although he was only fourteen when the older Glicka disappeared from his life, never forgot. Should the subject of Canada ever arise – it also rarely did – my father would always ponder an invisible point on the ceiling and, with a faraway cast in his eye, comment: "My cousin Glicka went to live there but, alas, she died." No doubt he also thought of his cousin Reuben, who had visited once from Montreal, but he rarely mentioned him or his siblings, whom he knew nothing about.

"Absence makes the heart grow fonder," my mother would sometimes say in rejoinder, a bit mysteriously and smiling wryly, but my father insisted she was the nicest of his cousins, the children of his Uncle Abe. My mother disapproved of Abe's flock, and with good reason. This large and unruly brood – the sons and daughters of Uncle Abe, who was himself no shining example, and his put-upon wife, the inexplicably named Gloria (so put-upon, in fact, that she died young, mysteriously so by all accounts) – were all wastrels or scoundrels, or had married ones.

Some of their children were already grown and they too seemed to be set on wayward or questionable paths. Only Glicka, who had disappeared from the scene early on, had, apparently, escaped the taint of her family.

My father's father was named Joseph and was always called that; but his younger brother Abraham was invariably called Abe. That in itself spoke volumes about the differences between the two men. Joseph had been the editor of a newspaper covering the burgeoning Jewish world of the Lower East Side, a respected columnist, a distinguished scholar whose multi-language library, encased behind glass doors in the study of his large Brooklyn apartment, fascinated me as a child. Abe had been the owner of a candy store in the Bronx and, during Prohibition, produced moonshine in his back room. As for their children, well, among my father's siblings were another journalist like him, a lawyer, a dental technician with his own denture business and the owner of a successful umbrella factory in Pennsylvania. Even my aunt Ida had married reasonably well, to a photographer who had his own shop. Abe's children, on the other hand, were in real estate and insurance sales – how low can you get? my mother would ask – and one, cousin Meyer, was actually in prison, for fraud. Another cousin, Murray, now in the trucking business, had gotten his start as a bootlegger at his father's knee. Among Glicka's sisters, one was married to a man who gave his occupation as accountant but was well known to be a bookmaker, while the other, now disgraced and living in Florida where no one knew her, had been briefly married to a schoolteacher who took an excessive interest in his female students. Compared to these, Glicka, who had merely moved to a distant country for love and died in childbirth, seemed like a saint.

All of this was largely academic – relations between the clan of Joseph and that of Abe had never been good, and after the deaths of the two old men, who had barely spoken to each other for years, the members of each camp mostly lost contact with the other. And, within the clan of Joseph itself, brothers and sister, who once had their aged parents as a focal point, also began drifting apart, seeing each other less and less frequently.

"This is a shame," said my mother, who herself came from a close family, and she invented a family circle to bring us all closer together.

"This will be nothing but toil, and heartache," my father cautioned, though he did it with a wink to us children, suggesting he wasn't completely serious. "When it comes to family, best to let sleeping bears lie."

But my mother persisted, and, for most of the Fifties and into the early Sixties, twice a year she would organize a large gathering of the descendants of Joseph and his good wife, Leah, whom I knew as *bubba*: once in the summer at Uncle Henry's lakeside cottage in the Catskills, and once in the winter, at the home of one or another of the New York uncles, Izzy or Sam or Henry, or our own apartment in Brooklyn, not far from where my grandparents had lived. These reunions would be attended by all of my father's siblings, even my uncle Nathan, in from Pennsylvania, and their spouses, children and the few grandchildren who had already appeared. They were pleasant enough, with plenty of good food, drink and talk, but it was generally conceded that, were it not for my mother, they wouldn't occur and the family, as a family, would likely cease to exist – which is exactly what eventually did happen when my mother died. But long before that, disharmony was sown by the approach to the family circle of our distant cousin Henrietta, whose existence had previously been unknown.

The letter was addressed to my mother and was postmarked in Whitehorse, YT, which, a quick search through the atlas revealed to be the Yukon Territory, in northern Canada. The name on the letter, Henrietta Dumont, was unfamiliar to all of us.

"Yukon," my father said with interest. He was fond of the novels and stories of Jack London, and could even recite a line or two from the poems of Robert Service.

"My dear cousin Bertie," the letter began, and at this point my father interrupted, "Cousin? Bertie, you have a cousin Henrietta? In Canada? *I* had a cousin who went to live there, as you know, but *you*? I didn't know that."

My mother had already read the letter once, to herself, and now was attempting to read it aloud to us all, at the dinner table, the meal having been completed and my sisters having finished clearing away the dishes and serving the coffee. "Let me read this, Harry," she said with mild exasperation.

"Who's stopping you?" my father protested.

My mother cleared her throat. "My dear cousin Bertie, We have never met, indeed you have probably never heard my name or known of my existence..."

"She's right so far," my father interrupted.

My mother glared at him over her glasses and went on. "I take the liberty of writing to you, though I am in fact a cousin of your husband..."

"*My* cousin!?"

"...because I understand that it is *you* who take responsibility for maintaining ties within the family."

Here my father kept silent, listening intently, but

Dave Margoshes

nodding his head gravely. The disasters he had seemed to predict hadn't materialized, but his ambivalent feelings about my mother's efforts with the family circle had persisted – he appreciated what she did, was grateful, but not entirely in favour.

My mother took the opportunity of my father's silence to clear her throat. Then she continued reading: "My mother was Glicka Larocque, who was a first cousin of your husband's, their respective fathers having been brothers. My mother and your husband played together as children. Indeed, she had the warmest regard for your husband."

Here, I should say, the dynamics of the table shifted, the mood changing palpably. My father leaned forward, his listening obviously growing more intense. My mother, on the other hand, frowned, as if there were an unpleasant taste in her mouth. She paused to take a sip of coffee, then read on.

"This I know not directly from my mother's lips, as she died in bringing me into this world, and I have had the bitter task of growing up as a motherless child..."

"So it's true," my father murmured, aloud but really to himself.

"...but from her hand, as I have acquired, after a long struggle with my brother – the less said about that the better – my mother's diary. It is from this remarkable volume that I have learned much about my mother's family and the world from which she sprang, the world which you, dear Berte, are now the self-appointed guardian of, the world to which I now aspire to belong to."

"Dangling prepositions," my sister Judy remarked at this point, setting off a brief argument between her and my sister Esther about the appropriateness of grammar in a family letter. Esther, the eldest and already in Brooklyn College, leaned towards the informal; Judy, still in her last year at New Utricht High School but the editor of the school newspaper, was a stickler for the rules. I myself was still in the "better seen than heard" stage of my childhood and had no views at all on grammar.

After my mother re-established order, we quickly learned the facts of our cousin Henrietta's life. My father's cousin Glicka had indeed fallen in love with a Canadian, just as family lore had always said. He was a fur trader, a former trapper, whom she had met during one of his trips to New York. His name was Armand Larocque, a Canadian mixed-blood of French and Indian stock, a people known as Metis, and, although that seemed unlikely, he claimed to be Jewish on his mother's side, believing her to be descended from one of the Lost Tribes of Israel – my father inexplicably guffawed when he heard that. Glicka had accompanied this man to a city far to the west and north called Edmonton, where they established a small but comfortable home. Her husband was often away on business, either further north acquiring furs, or in the south cultivating markets, and it was during one of these absences that, having already produced two healthy children, Glicka had a delivery with complications that resulted in the birth of Henrietta and her own death. Armand Larocque came home from the north to find himself a widower and the father of three orphans. The infant was named after his own mother, with Glicka as her middle name.

According to Henrietta's detailed account, which my mother continued to read, Larocque remained in Edmonton less than a year before moving further north, to the frontier community of Labeche, where he would be closer to his suppliers. To deal with the children, he took a new wife, an Eskimo woman he called Rose of Sharon. This woman, Henrietta wrote, was kind and thoughtful, but absent-minded and restless "and no true substitute for a real mother."

"My poor girl," my father said, receiving a skeptical glance from my mother in return.

To make matters worse, Henrietta and her brother, Abram, were always at odds – "he blamed me for our mother's death," she wrote – and the unpleasantness between them, along with their father's frequent absences and their stepmother's frequent indifference, made for an unhappy childhood. (Oddly, there was no further mention of the third sibling.) To escape the squalid life at Lebeche, Henrietta married young, to a special constable of the Royal Canadian Mounted Police, Marcus Dumont, a fine man who, like her, was partially of native blood. Her life with Dumont proved to be an eventful one, as he was posted to a number of different northern locales during his brief career, which had recently come to a surprising, tragic end during an encounter with a polar bear. The details, she wrote, were too painful to go into. At any rate, she now found herself a widow, the mother of two small children, living in respectable but extremely modest means on a small government pension in an isolated outpost. "Besides myself and my children, and a kind gentleman named Dr. Isadore Birkowitz, a dentist who has befriended us, there are no Jews here in Whitehorse," she wrote. Having recently acquired her mother's diary, after the previously mentioned legal battle with her brother, she was now filled with longing to establish contact with her family and the larger world of Jewry. "My children deserve this," she wrote, a statement which, in its simple eloquence, touched us all, even me.

There was a long discussion at the table about the

events and personalities depicted in the letter. Grammar aside, Judy thought many of the letter's elements were romantic; Esther tended to be more cynical. It was my father who wondered how Henrietta had learned of the family circle and my mother's leading role in it, no less our address – none of this, obviously, would have been in her mother's diary. A thorough rereading of the letter confirmed the absence of any such mention. But all that aside, we all agreed that Henrietta's letter was gripping and could not be ignored.

Ironically, though, the plight of my father's cousin galvanized not my father but my mother. With my father's encouragement, she began an immediate correspondence with cousin Henrietta. She prepared a newsletter that repeated the salient points of Henrietta's story and circulated it among not only the members of the established family circle but tracked down and made contact with that darker side of the family, the descendants of my father's Uncle Abe, with whom there had been little communication for years. At the next family gathering, which, as it happened, came just a month or two following the arrival of Henrietta's first letter, places were set for this absent cousin and her children, just as, at the *seders* of many religious Jews, a place is set for the absent prophet Elijah. My mother prepared cards, on which she wrote the names "Henrietta," "Uglik" and "Toogl" – the children apparently had been given Eskimo names – and placed them on the empty plates, as a reminder to all. Most significant of all, she put a bowl next to Henrietta's empty plate, into which, she made it clear, donations were to be placed. It wasn't clear what exactly the donations were for, since the distance between New York and Whitehorse seemed enormous, but a travel fund of some sort was mentioned.

My mother, who had only recently emerged from a

life dominated by caring for her children to return to work, having obtained a two-thirds-time secretarial position at a public school nearby, was much caught up in, as my father termed it, "this Canadian cousin business." I couldn't recall ever having seen her so energized.

My father, who, as a newspaper reporter, was skeptical, even cynical, by inclination, was, as ever with matters of family, ambivalent. He was enthusiastic about making contact with this new-found cousin, but raised suspicions. "What do we really know about this woman, Bertie?" he asked. And it was true. There did appear to be discrepancies and puzzles in her story, particularly her knowledge of the family circle.

"Perhaps her husband tracked us down," my sister Judy offered, and it did seem reasonable that her connection to the police world might give her access to otherwise private information, but my father remained skeptical, pointing out that Henrietta's written chronology left unclear which came first, the acquiring of her mother's diary or her husband's untimely death.

"Perhaps the dentist, Dr...?" my mother suggested.

"Birko-something."

"Maybe he has connections in New York..." Her voice trailed off.

My father shrugged. "Is this yearning for family going to cost money?" he asked.

"*Harry*," my mother replied crossly. "This is *your* cousin, daughter of your darling Glicka. Remember?"

"She was a good woman, Glicka," my father conceded, his eyes taking on a faraway cast.

My mother's crusade – such were its dimensions as it developed – soon became clear: to bring Henrietta and her children to New York, where they could take their rightful places within their immediate and larger families. This would be a monumental task – "This is

crazy, Bertie!" my father cried when he first heard it –
as the moving expenses would be prohibitive and it was
questionable whether Henrietta's pension, meagre as it
was, would be able to follow her to another country.

"Who knows if her children can even speak English," my father complained, seeking and finding objec-
tions. "Probably they speak Eskimo. They eat raw fish."

My mother laughed with a combination of exasperation and humour. "You spoke no English when you
came here," she sweetly reminded him. "And isn't pickled herring your favourite *forshpeiz*?"

My father didn't like to be corrected when he was
wrong, especially by my mother, from whom he had
higher expectations. He sulked. But he was a reasonable
man, a fair man, and gradually he came around. Although
labour was his regular beat, he had a nose for a good
human interest story, and he wrote an article for *The
Day* about this distant cousin – "this adventuress at the
furthest outpost of Jewry," as he described her, dubbing
Whitehorse the "north-westernmost neighbourhood of
the Lower East Side" – and soon Henrietta was a *cause
célèbre* in Manhattan, Brooklyn, Queens and the Bronx.
The New York Times picked up the story, offering a short
item. Letters to the editor in the Yiddish press cham-
pioned Henrietta's case, and my father enlisted the
services of his brother Henry, the attorney, to look into
the legal aspects of her immigration.

As a side issue, a spirited debate ignited in the letters to the editor column of *The Day* about the validity
of the Lost Tribes of Israel theory. One distinguished
rabbi, a professor at the theological seminary, wrote an
article arguing that the Indians of the American and
Canadian West and North were indeed Jews. This was
clear from their physical appearance, their languages
and many of their customs. Another rabbi, equally dis-

tinguished, responded with a blistering letter dismembering his colleague's thesis and strongly implying that the first rabbi was in league with the devil, the fascists or both. "At the very least, this hare-brained theory offers dangerous succour to the anti-Semites," he wrote. Others wrote letters arguing pro and con whether the government of Canada was allied with the Soviet Union; whether the Royal Canadian Mounted Police, with their famous red serge jackets, were an offshoot of the Red Army; whether cousin Henrietta and her two small children were likely or not to be Communists and, if so, Trotskyites.

At the next gathering of the family circle, many of the previously estranged cousins – the children and grandchildren of Abe, second and third cousins I had heard of but never met – were present, noisily and amiably, embracing their more discreet cousins, the descendents of Joseph. This gathering took place at Uncle Henry's cottage, it now being summer, and a good thing too, my father said, because no one's home in the city would have been nearly big enough. "We'll have to rent Madison Square Garden when she finally gets here," he predicted sourly.

The mention of Madison Square Garden, the home of numerous sporting events, perked up the ears of cousin-in-law Lou, the bookmaker, and soon he was offering odds on when Henrietta would be returned to the bosom of her long-lost family. It had come that far – *when*, no longer *if.* The donations bowl, marked with a handwritten card, "The Henrietta Fund," overflowed.

"At our next family party, cousin Henrietta will be the honoured guest," my mother announced, and this repeated piece of news rippled through the large crowd like a mantra of the dimensions of the age-old Jewish prediction, part plea, part boast, "Next year in Jerusalem."

Contributions poured in as well from complete strangers, newspaper readers who were touched by Henrietta's plight. Her story appealed to widows, orphans, star-crossed lovers and people with distant beloved relatives. "And who does that leave out?" my father wondered.

During the preparation of his newspaper story, my father had done simple research and learned some salient facts that had again aroused his suspicions: Whitehorse, rather than being a tiny outpost on the edge of an ice floe, was a thriving small city of some ten thousand people, the capital and administrative centre of the territory, with many urban amenities, even a daily newspaper of its own, the *Star*. My father telephoned a reporter there, resulting in a story in that paper as well. One thing he learned was that, despite cousin Henrietta's claim that she, her children and the friendly dentist were the only Jews there, Whitehorse had a small but cohesive Jewish community, made up of teachers, doctors and merchants. "Staten Island could be worse," my father mused.

In Henrietta's defence, my mother pointed out that the far-flung cousin lived not in Whitehorse itself, but the tiny village of Princess Anne Island, a daylong dogsled mush from the capital. It was there that her late husband, Constable Dumont, had been posted, there that he died, there that the widowed Henrietta remained.

"She could maybe move to Whitehorse," my father half suggested, but my mother had her sights and heart set on restoring the woman to the family fold, on closing the circle.

"What about cousin Florence?" my father asked,

only half jokingly. That was a low blow, Florence being the former wife of the child molester, who had disappeared into the jungles of Florida. She was just as far-flung, just as alienated from her family, just as deserving as Henrietta, wasn't that so? "And, in all likelihood, an innocent bystander."

True, my mother admitted, but Florence had absented herself from the family on her own accord. "Henrietta is a victim of circumstances."

And what, my father teased, about Henrietta's nasty brother, Abram, and her sister, who had never been named to us and was hardly mentioned? Weren't they also victims of circumstances? Didn't they too deserve to be saved?

"No," my mother pronounced, making it clear there was no doubt in her mind. "They haven't reached out."

"But shouldn't *we* reach out to *them*?" my father insisted. He was playing with fire and probably knew it, but he had a reckless streak.

My mother wouldn't be baited, though. "You may be right, Harry. Maybe later. We'll see what happens."

Who could argue with that?

Eventually, all the details were worked out, my mother being terrifyingly efficient. Passports and visas were obtained – it turned out that Henrietta, through her mother, was still a U.S. citizen, as were her children. Travel arrangements were made – a combination of bush plane and railroad. Temporary lodging was secured – my mother would have liked to offer our hospitality, but our cramped apartment on Eastern Parkway barely contained us, and certainly had no room for extended visitors. Instead, distant cousin Barney, the real-estate salesman who now had his own agency, had offered the mother-in-law suite in his Bronx brownstone row house, his own mother-in-law having recently remarried. It was assumed that Henrietta and her children could live there, rent free, until she was settled and found a place of her own. One of the children was already of school age, and enrolment at the nearest public school had also been arranged. Even more importantly, distant cousin Ben had opened up a job for Henrietta in the office of his used car lot, Honest Abe's, named in honour of his father. Henrietta had told us in one of her letters that, serving at her husband's side in remote outports, she had handled the paperwork for the detachment, looking after supplies and records, and had developed decent secretarial skills, although "maybe not by civilized standards," she had joked.

"So who said Honest Abe's car lot is civilized?" my father rejoined.

Finally, all was in place and the day for Henrietta's arrival in New York drew near. It was winter again, Thanksgiving and the holiday season both having passed, and the bleakness of January and February stretched ahead. The far-flung cousins' arrival would certainly do a lot to brighten those drab months, for my mother, at the very least. More than two years had passed since we'd first heard from Henrietta, and she and my mother had exchanged numerous letters. It was as if they two were cousins, *close* cousins.

Madison Square Garden was apparently beyond our reach, but through the good offices of Lou, the bookmaker in-law, a union hall on the Grand Concourse in the Bronx had been made available, at no cost. My mother had been able, with minimal effort, to twist the arms of a long list of female cousins who would be cooking and baking their specialties. Distant cousin Murray, who had kept up his distillery connections though he was now, by all accounts, a legitimate businessman, would be providing the wine. The party would be, it appeared, the family reunion to end all family reunions. Everyone would be there, even distant cousin Meyer, who had recently been released from Sing Sing on parole. Rumour had it that even cousin Florence from Florida might be making an appearance, the first time in the dozen years since she'd begun her self-exile. If she did appear, my father pointed out, there would be a certain justice to it.

"That cousin of yours," he said, referring to Henrietta as if she were in fact my mother's cousin, although she was his, "might do more than anyone could have imagined to bring our family together."

My mother was not an "I-told-you-so" sort, so she said nothing, but even I, who was halfway between my tenth and eleventh birthdays, could see that her smile was smug.

The moment we'd all been waiting for arrived. Henrietta and her children had several days earlier embarked on a long, complicated journey that began with a bush plane to Whitehorse, followed by commercial airline to Edmonton, then by train coach south to the improbably named Cut Knife, Montana, then east on the Empire Builder through Minneapolis, Chicago and Cleveland to Grand Central Station in New York where, mid-afternoon on a snowy but mild Thursday, my mother and I impatiently awaited them.

"They'll feel right at home," I had said, on seeing the fresh snow as my mother and I emerged from our apartment house and walked to the car, a 1950 De Soto station wagon cousin Ben had lent us for the occasion. My mother smiled indulgently at my comment. She worked mornings and into mid-afternoon usually, but had come home early, and I had been allowed to stay home from school after lunch as well.

Henrietta's children, who my parents had calculated

were my fourth cousins, were far younger than me, Uglik, seven, and Toogl, five, and my mother had instructed me to be especially nice to them. No one said this aloud, but I was sure that poor Uglik must be called "Ugly" by other kids. Poor guy, I thought.

The station was crowded and my mother worried how we would all recognize each other, although she had specified, in her final letter to Henrietta, that we would meet them beneath the big clock. There were two big clocks in the station, but we took up a position beneath the one closest to the arrival gates from the west, along with hundreds of other people who had apparently given the same directions to their distant cousins. I wondered if these particular distant relatives didn't perhaps tell time by the sun and wouldn't know what a clock was, but I kept this thought to myself. I assumed my fourth cousins, and perhaps Henrietta herself, would be wearing fur coats, perhaps even snowshoes, and that there would be no trouble recognizing them.

So imagine my disappointment when we finally stood face to face, I awkwardly patting the backs of two scruffy-looking children in ordinary corduroy jackets and scuffed Thom McCann shoes, my mother embracing a drab, shapeless woman in a kerchief and cloth coat and inexplicably carrying a yellow umbrella.

"Henrietta!"

"Berte!"

"And these must be Uglik and Toogl. You must be exhausted, darlings." My mother stooped to embrace them both in a hug.

"And this must be David." Cousin Henrietta's breath, when her face touched mine, was strong with SenSen. Getting a close look at her face, I could see that she was quite a bit younger than my mother, although at my own age I had a difficult time discerning the ages of adults, especially women.

"You're here," my mother said. "You're finally here."

"We're here. I can hardly believe it." Henrietta spoke with an accent that was unusual but hardly exotic.

"Can we have ice cream?" Uglik asked. There was a smudge of dirt on the end of his nose, and his skin was darker than mine by a shade or two, but no more so than that of an Italian boy I knew, and there was nothing particularly foreign-looking about him, or about Toogl, who had shiny black pigtails to match shiny black eyes and clung shyly to her mother's leg. They were certainly nothing like the Red Indians I'd seen in movies.

We chatted like this all the way on the car ride to the Bronx as pure white flakes of snow, large as any I'd ever seen, fell gently on the De Soto, as if to make the visitors feel at home. "This is a wonderful car," Henrietta said in an awestruck tone, looking around the front seat and running her hand over the dashboard. She mentioned that Dr. Birkowitz, the dentist who had figured occasionally in her letters, had a fine car too.

"A Lincoln. And you'd think the men who work on cars in garages, the...mechanics? The mechanics would be happy to work on such on a fine car, but no. They're happiest with trucks and jeeps."

"If you want to buy a car, I'm sure cousin Ben will find you a good buy," my mother said. "Uncle Ben, that is. He's your uncle."

"I must learn to drive," Henrietta said, laughing gaily. "Goodness, there's *so much* to learn."

She turned on the radio and Johnny Ray's "Cry," which had been all the rage for weeks, came blaring out. "Oh, my goodness," Henrietta said, as if she'd been stung, and quickly turned it off.

My mother and I, and cousin Barney and his wife
and children, big lumbering teenagers who had little
interest in us, saw to their getting settled in, and we all
sat down at a large table in Barney's living room to dinner, which wasn't very good, the unidentified meat
tough and the vegetables overcooked. Still, I thought
with satisfaction of the reheated chicken giblet and
noodle casserole my father and sisters would be eating
at home. Henrietta and her children ate with gusto and
consumed everything put before them, asking for seconds, and Henrietta heaped praise on the meal and
asked Barney's wife, Anna, for the recipes.

"The poor things look half starved," my mother said
as we drove home. She had sent them plenty of money
for meals on the trip, though, so that couldn't be the
reason. My mother turned to me and spoke as if I were
an adult: "We've exchanged so many letters, but I really
don't know Henrietta at all."

The frankness of that confession sent a small shiver
through me and that night as I lay in bed awaiting
sleep I thought how little I knew my mother, and my
father and sisters as well. I'd thought I did – if I
thought about it at all – just as I'd thought I knew my
larger family, who was who and what was what. Now
I realized differently.

The family circle gathering was that Sunday and gave
me my first appreciation of the word "anticlimactic."

Everyone was there, even cousin Florence from
Florida, even paroled cousin Meyer – apparently there
were no known felons in the family so he was free to
associate with us. The spirits of my grandfather, Joseph,
and his brother Abraham, if they were about, would

have been pleased, perhaps even proud, to see the large gathering of their children, grandchildren, even great-grandchildren. Joseph and Abe had come to America alone and with nothing, and just look at what they had started.

But they might have been dismayed to see the hole in the centre of the family circle.

People were happy to see Meyer and Florence – despite Meyer's indiscretions and those of Florence's former husband, they were loved members of their own clan, the children of Abe – but the cousins of both clans were less than enthralled with Henrietta and her children. No one knew her, after all, and there were few points of common interest. Though she seemed ordinary enough, the circumstances of her life were certainly worlds apart from those of her New York relatives. Everyone was on best manners, approaching the far-flung cousin and making polite conversation. Then they moved on.

Henrietta was wearing a loose-fitting almost colourless dress, much like the housedresses my mother wore on cleaning day, and stockings with crooked seams and high heels that thrust her already awkward body forward, making it appear as if she was constantly about to topple over. This impression was augmented by an impressively large bosom for a woman so otherwise slender. In her mousy brown hair, which covered her head like a tumbleweed, she'd pinned a paper flower and she'd sprayed herself with a perfume that smelled as much like dead meat as anything.

This smell also clung to Uglik and Toogl – redubbed Arthur and Emily – thus reviving my fantasy that they gnawed on whale blubber as a snack. Instead, I watched as they consumed huge portions of chicken, dumplings, salad and *challah* at the sit-down dinner, and potato chips, pretzels and soda pop the rest of the day. Arthur wore new dungarees and a polo shirt, new U.S. Keds sneakers. His black hair was pomaded and brushed till it gleamed but refused to stay in place. He was painfully ordinary and shy, a seven-year-old boy of little interest to me, and, despite my mother's admonition that I was to pay special attention to him, for the most part I ignored him. For most of the afternoon, he sat on the floor in a corner shuffling a deck of bubblegum baseball cards I'd given him, old ones or seconds I had no need for. Emily, though, had overcome her initial shyness and fallen in with two grandchildren of her own age. Dressed in almost identical pink frocks with ribbons, making it hard to tell which one was Emily, the three of them spent the afternoon chasing each other under the tables and chairs, shrieking.

Naturally, there was much talk of Glicka, especially among the children of Abe. She had been their beloved, if only half-remembered, baby sister, but there was little their niece Henrietta could add to what she'd already written in her letters, which my mother had circulated. She herself, after all, had never known her mother. Cousins Barney and Ben and Murray and Florence and the others asked questions about Glicka that Henrietta couldn't answer, but she asked none of her own. She had read her mother's diary – which she had neglected to bring with her from Princess Anne Island – and apparently was satisfied with that. Nor did she appear to have much interest in her aunts and uncles and cousins.

No one asked Henrietta what had become of Armand Larocque, their fur-trading brother- or cousin-in-law, or Rose of Sharon, his second wife, nor was there any mention of brother Abram or the unnamed sister, as much their long-lost niece and cousin as Henrietta.

Nor was the recently deceased Constable Dumont much in people's thoughts or conversations.

People did ask about life in the North, of course. But when they learned that Henrietta and her children did not live in an igloo or ride around on a dogsled, they soon lost interest.

For several hours, people milled around at the party without actually connecting, speaking to each other without listening. I could see from the frown on my mother's face that her original estimation of Abe's side of the family had been reconfirmed, and that she was disappointed with the closer group of her in-laws. Even my favourite, Uncle Henry, usually so gregarious, was unusually reticent. He loved to do magic tricks for children, pulling pennies from their ears and noses, but I didn't see him performing for Arthur or Emily. It was as if, in the presence of something at once so foreign and so familiar, Uncle Henry had become discombobulated – a delicious word I had recently learned from my sisters. The rest of the family seemed equally stricken.

"They don't care," my mother pouted to my father.

"No, they don't," he agreed. He himself had quickly lost interest in Henrietta. Later, he would pronounce her as unattractive and charmless a woman as he'd ever met, but my mother would always say he was being unfair.

"This is a woman raised by an Eskimo," my mother would retort.

But wouldn't that have made her fascinating rather than dull? I wondered. And later, when I moved to Canada myself as an adult, when I traveled to Whitehorse, when I learned more about the North, as Canadians inevitably do, my cousin Henrietta, by then dead and her children lost to me, grew in my estimation. I would have liked to have met them all again, have another chance, and I regretted not having tried harder to befriend them when I did have a chance. Well, I was only a boy myself.

As it turned out, the family circle gathering broke up earlier than we'd expected. The weather was poor, with ice and slush on the streets and more snow threatening, and people began to make excuses early in the evening. They bundled up and disappeared into the Bronx night. Henrietta and her children went home with cousin Barney and his family after an extended goodbye with my mother, hugging and kissing and promising to talk soon, see you soon.

"I owe you so much," Henrietta told my mother, and that seemed to me to be very much the truth.

"It was nothing," my mother replied. "No, it was a pleasure."

My mother was quiet on the long subway ride home, the De Soto having been returned to cousin Ben's lot. So was my father, although he did deliver himself of one pronouncement, "No, it was duty," which elicited a dirty look from my mother. Even my sisters, both sophisticated college girls now, with something to say about everything, usually, were quiet. I sat silently between my parents and watched through the window the subway tunnel markers flashing by, imagining I was in a bush plane and they were ice floes.

My mother did talk to Henrietta on the phone, several times, in the weeks that followed, and had lunch with her once, in Manhattan, but she reported little of what they'd talked about at the dinner table. They continued to exchange Chanukah cards for several years, but that was all. The mystery of how Henrietta had become aware of my mother and found our address remained unsolved.

Dave Margoshes

Henrietta worked at Honest Abe's used car lot only a few weeks before she found another job, and moved quickly from cousin Barney's mother-in-law suite. She disappeared into the jungles of the Bronx as deeply as Florence had into those of Florida, to which she'd returned after the family gathering. We never saw either of those cousins again, although we heard a report – second, maybe even third hand – that Henrietta had married again and moved, like Florence, to Florida. And at the next family circle gathering, the following summer at Uncle Henry's, the descendents of my father's Uncle Abe were not present.

My mother didn't abandon the idea of the family circle, but she seemed content to allow it to grow smaller.

She rarely mentioned Henrietta again, and the subject of the campaign to rescue her from the wilds of the North and the subsequent reunion became a sort of semi-taboo subject in our household. If someone made a reference to it, my mother would usually look away and my father would shake his head and frown, placing his finger against his nose. If my father had carried a faint torch for his lost cousin Glicka, then it was my mother who seemed to have been smitten and later disappointed with Glicka's daughter. A few years later when I, a teenager now, had my first unhappy experience with love, I thought of my mother and Henrietta again – yes, it was as if my mother had been spurned by a lover. But such a thought made me far too uncomfortable to dwell on it for long.

Afterword: Listening to My Father

I became a writer early in the summer I was thirteen – actually, a couple of weeks before my thirteenth birthday. I remember clearly the precise moment. I had been writing before that, little sketches and simple stories, or pieces of stories I'd abandon after a few pages scribbled in my notebook, but mostly I'd merely been *thinking* about writing.

At this particular moment, I became an actual writer.

I spent that weekend with my father in Atlantic City.

He used to go out of town occasionally on assignments for the newspaper where he worked, *The Day*, which covered the world of the Lower East Side and the larger Jewish community of New York City and environs, some three million people in the larger pool of some ten million. He covered the labour beat and regularly went to the conventions of the men's and ladies' garment workers, the largest unions in New York, which in those days were largely made up of Jews, and of the American Federation of Labor, the umbrella group that brought all the major American unions together. Those national conventions, which lasted a week or more, were sometimes held in places like Miami or Chicago, but the garment workers preferred to stay closer to home, so Atlantic City was a favourite choice.

This year, he asked me if I'd like to join him for the

weekend. Of course, I was thrilled, and on a Friday in June I took a bus down to the New Jersey shore to join him – he'd already been there for several days. School had not yet finished for the summer and I had first to endure an excruciatingly long day of endless classes before being freed at three and racing home to pick up the small overnight bag I'd borrowed from one of my sisters. It was already packed, stuffed with a few clothes, my swimsuit, a toothbrush and toothpaste in a plastic bag, a notebook and ballpoint pen, and a book to read, a collection of stories by Damon Runyon, whom I was mad for that year, along with O'Henry and Saki and Jack London. My mother, who didn't get off work until four, had left me a note, which I found on the kitchen table, propped up against the sugar bowl: "Travel safely, dear. Don't forget to have something to eat before you go. *Listen to your father*" – that sentence was underlined. "Have a wonderful time." At that stage of my life, I got along well with my father but wasn't as close to him as I was to my mother, and I suspected that the trip had been her idea, in pursuit of what's now known as "male bonding," that she'd persuaded my father into it.

I checked my wallet – my mother had given me a ten dollar bill for the bus fare and spending money, and some change for the subway the night before – and quickly ate an apple. Then I set out.

We lived on Eastern Parkway in Brooklyn, on the top floor of a four-floor walk-up – it would be three more years before my parents would fulfill their dream of moving back to the country and take us to a house already being built in western New Jersey. I walked west on the parkway to Kingston Avenue and took the subway into Manhattan to the Port Authority Building, the sprawling bus terminal in Times Square, where I caught a bus to Atlantic City. There was a lineup for

Dave Margoshes

the bus, crowded with weekend holiday-goers, and I stood behind a kid with a portable radio jangling with rock and roll. He was older than me, sixteen or seventeen, with a slicked-back duck's ass haircut and a tight-fitting white T-shirt, its sleeves rolled up above his biceps like Marlon Brando in *The Wild One* or James Dean in *Rebel Without A Cause*, this kid himself like someone stepping out of movies that would come later; *West Side Story* or *Grease*. It gave me an odd sliver of pleasure standing so close to this kid, whom older people around us were eying with distaste, hoping that perhaps some of these critical people would think we were together, although he was oblivious to me.

That was just the start of the feeling of exhilaration I had all that afternoon and evening, all that weekend, in fact: being on my own, riding the bus, occasionally glimpsing blue waves as the bus skirted close to the ocean, the rock and roll continuing to pour from the kid's radio, just across the aisle from me – Bill Haley's "Rock Around the Clock" was a hit that spring and it was being played repeatedly on the two-hour bus ride – joining my father, staying at a hotel, enjoying the bracing view of girls in swimsuits on the beach, eating in a restaurant – I had my first club sandwich on the first night, a steak dinner on the second – and being introduced to people by my father as "my son," which filled me with a delicious mixture of embarrassment and pride.

This was the first time, I think, that I'd ever been around so many strange adults. Children live in a child's world – the only adults they know, usually, are parents, relatives, neighbours, teachers – people they take for granted and don't find very interesting. Now I found myself sitting in the hotel coffee shop with my father and his friends, reporters and low-level union functionaries, having a late supper – that club sandwich, layers of turkey, ham and bacon on two slices of white bread, the third of brown, quartered on a diagonal, each piece skewered with a toothpick festooned with either a pimento-stuffed green olive or a pickled white onion and a swirl of red ribbon, with crisp french fries, and a tall glass of ginger ale with ice – what a luxury.

Sitting at our table, or stopping by to say hello during the course of our meal, was a cast of memorable characters who might have stepped out of the pages of the Damon Runyon stories I'd been reading on the bus, including a man who had lost a hand while fighting in the Spanish Civil War and a man who had been a Communist and now was, my father said later – this was his phrase – a "rabid anti-communist." There was a man who'd been a gangster and earned a reputation breaking strikes but now worked for a union and was, my father said, "a pretty decent chap," and a reporter from *The New York Times*, whom I remembered reading about, a man who'd been blinded when gangsters threw acid in his face. And of course my father's colleague Vogel, who covered labour for the rival Yiddish paper, *The Forward*. The two had been friends for so long they could almost anticipate the ends of each other's sentences and there was a warm familiarity between them I was drawn to. I had met Vogel several times and, invariably, he would scrutinize me with a narrow-eyed gaze, then turn to my father with a quizzical, "Morgenstern, this is a son?"

A handsome couple particularly caught my attention, a man and a woman holding hands – the woman a lovely blonde with very sad hazel eyes – who my father told me only met at gatherings like this because they each had families at home. "They married the wrong people," my father said with a wink, leaving me to ponder the mysterious implications.

I started thinking about these fascinating people, of course, and, inevitably, began to write stories about them in my head – I say "inevitably," which is how, in retrospect, it seems to me; perhaps, in reality, it was more a matter of chance. If so, then that was a serendipitous piece of chance indeed. Whenever I had a few minutes alone, I jotted down ideas and descriptions in my notebook. The next day, Saturday, while my father covered meetings, I was on my own, walking the Boardwalk and the beach, going for a swim, eating a hotdog loaded with onions and peppers, eying the girls in shorts and halter tops along the amusement park area – some of them my age, some of them older, their bodies riper and even more of a mystery to me. All through the day, I was alive to the sights and sounds swirling around me, coming to me through a new filter, and my head was filled with a jumble of images, faces, voices. It was the voices I paid attention to most.

Heading back to the hotel in late afternoon, I caught sight of that couple I'd started to think of as The Star-Crossed Lovers: "They married the wrong people," my father had said. How that inflamed my imagination. They were coming out through the door of a hotel far smaller than the one my father and I were staying at, onto the boardwalk. I was aware there were various innocent explanations – a drink with friends, a convention-related meeting – but I chose to believe the more romantic possibility, that only moments before they had been entwined in each other's naked arms and legs on a bed, while a small electric fan on the dresser stirred the slenderest of breezes in the hot saline air.

I paused to scribble that line down, *"while a small electric fan on the dresser stirred the slenderest of breezes in the hot saline air,"* entranced by the image of the fan – I could see the desultory swing of its blades, hear the faint whine of its oil-deprived motor. Then I hurried to catch up with them as they strolled along the boardwalk, and followed them, at a safe distance, for several blocks, until they disappeared through the door of yet another small hotel, thoroughly confusing me. Had they been coming from an assignation (a word I'd recently learned) or going to one? I knew so little – at thirteen – about the possibilities of these intricate arrangements of the heart that I had no recourse but to fall back on imagination.

I've already described this couple as handsome, and they were that, middle-aged, perhaps even in their fifties, but very well put together, the woman a lovely blonde with the striking legs of a dancer flashing beneath her soft flowered skirt; the man tall and lean, with a full head of greying hair and wire-rimmed glasses that gave him the look of Henry Fonda in a courtroom film I'd seen not long before. He was in his shirtsleeves, the sleeves rolled up, and carried the jacket of his seersucker suit over his arm and his panama hat in his right hand, using his left to steer his companion loosely by the waist while her right hand lay lightly on his bare forearm, just ahead of the folded jacket. I saw all of this with remarkable clarity and made mental notes – to be transferred into written form in my notebook as soon as I could – with precision.

The couple gave off an aura that implied that love affairs such as theirs were the exclusive jurisdiction of beautiful people, a misapprehension it would take me some time to disabuse myself of. When they disappeared into the second hotel, I felt bereft, as if I'd been cut off from some amazing, slightly illicit adventure.

That evening, wearing a white shirt tucked into my neatly pressed chinos, I sat with my father and some of

Dave Margoshes

his friends – the mis-married couple not among them, to my regret – at a table in a banquet hall, eating a heavy meal, listening to speeches, watching people dancing later as my father drank rye and ginger ale after rye and ginger ale, and I sipped on a glass that, without benefit of the whisky, looked exactly like his, another small source of pleasure. Vogel sat between us, a small, owl-eyed man with a permanent smear of perspiration on his forehead, and their conversation slipped in and out of Yiddish, inadvertently excluding me and allowing my mind to wander. I was already drunk on conversation, and the incomprehensible sound of their voices formed a pleasing background as, my thoughts racing, I concocted stories about some of the people around me.

Sunday morning, my father was up early to cover yet another meeting, leaving me to sleep in, and later we had brunch together in the hotel dining room: ham and eggs with a strange sauce, pastries, fresh fruit, more luxuries. We walked together on the Boardwalk for an hour, my father's voice rising and falling in the wind like the seagulls that followed us, always hopeful for a crust of bread or something richer, and then he saw me onto the bus. He still had another few days of the convention.

That afternoon, on the long bus ride home, using a ballpoint pen emblazoned with the name of the hotel we'd stayed at and one of the steno pads my father took notes on, I began writing a story about several of the people I'd met – somehow, in the sluice of my imagination, the former Communist and the married man who loved the married woman merged and became one character, and the former gangster and the blinded columnist developed a grudging friendship. It was a fanciful story, very much in the style of Runyon, but completely different from anything I'd written before.

Until then, my attempts at writing had focused on

dogs and horses and ghosts – starting at about age ten, I had been very much in the thrall, in rapid succession, of Albert Payson Terhune with his magnificent collies, Thorne Smith and his debonair ghosts and Booth Tarkington and his trenchcoat-wearing Penrod. But on this particular weekend, I graduated to writing about real people, doing real things, with only a restrained tinge of the romantic colours that had become available to me. The intoxicating power the story cast over me was both exhilarating and frightening.

That was the first real story I'd ever tried to write, but even before that, two nights before, I'd had the crystalline moment in which I realized that I was a writer.

My father and I shared a hotel room – it had two twin beds – and as we'd prepared for bed Friday night, lining up in the bathroom to brush our teeth and use the toilet, I realized that this was the first time since I was little and used sometimes to crawl into bed with my parents that I'd slept in the same room as my father. We undressed together, and that too was a rarity. Summers, we often went to swim at Coney Island, and, when I was younger, he and I would change into our swimsuits together in a public dressing room filled with jostling naked men and boys. I realized I'd never been alone for so long with my father and I'd never been so close to him.

My father had married late and I was the last of my parents' children. He was about fifty when I was born, and on this weekend he was already in his sixties, his body going soft, his hair thin and grey.

My father's own father, my grandfather, whom I hadn't known well, had died only a couple of months earlier. I hadn't felt much at his passing, and was aware that my lack of tears had caused my father some distress. But I'd been conscious of my father's sadness, which still seemed to envelop him. I was also extremely conscious, in a way I'd never been before, of death, its power, inevitability and finality.

I saw my father's body in a new light that night in the hotel room and, as we lay in our beds in the darkness, my father's voice drifting disembodied in the air above us, talking about the people I'd met that evening, I was struck suddenly and sharply by the certain and unexpected knowledge that he would die – something that, happily, wasn't to happen for more than twenty years – and I was washed over with a powerful, ineffable sense of sadness and loss, almost as if the loss had already occurred. It was absolutely the strongest emotion I'd ever had in relation to my father and it shook me.

But at the very same time that I was feeling this unutterable sadness, I was also thinking about how to write about the experience and the feeling, about finding a way, somehow, of expressing what seemed to be inexpressible, and I was already, in my head, actually starting to do just that.

"'Tomorrow we'll walk on the boardwalk and watch the waves,' the man said in the darkness," I wrote in my mind.

"That will be good," I had the son respond, somewhat woodenly.

"Good night, son."

"Good night, Dad."

Was that my father and I speaking – actual voices hurling words into the darkness of the humming air-conditioned hotel room – or the father and son I was creating, the creatures of my imagination? I didn't know.

Up until that point, I realized – not then, but later – I had been attracted to writing because of the writing itself, the thrill of manipulating language – what at writers' conferences and university creative writing programs we refer to as craft, although I didn't have much of it at the time. But there are two other important parts to writing, parts I hadn't even been aware of, and I had just stumbled onto them: I now had something very specific I wanted to write about, and a vision of how I wanted to express it. Along with craft, I was now dimly conscious of art.

My father was talking – a real person, saying real words – but in my head, I was turning him into a character, turning his words into dialogue, thinking about how to get it right. That seemed enormously important.

I was reminded of that note my mother left: *Listen to your father*, she'd written. At that age, thirteen, I'd somehow gotten out of the habit of listening to him; it was a patience I now realized I needed to relearn. I started again to listen to my father that weekend; I've been listening to him – even over the thirty-five years since his death – and trying to get it right, ever since.

I've been working on a series of stories about the character I call "my father" – loosely based on my own father – for about thirty years. Over that time, many of them have been published in magazines and several in previous short story collections. I had no intention of doing a series, but I liked that first story – it was "The False Moustache" – a lot and wondered if I could use the character in other situations. The story had begun with a spark of truth – a story my father had told many times about a foolish man he'd once known – and the spirit of my father, who had died a couple of years earlier. I had a number of such yarns from my father rattling around in my head, and I soon wrote several more of my own "versions." Gradually, over many years, I began to think I might have enough of these tales eventually to fill a book.

All of the stories begin, first of all, with the character of Morgenstern, "my father," who is very much imbued with the persona and personality of my own father, and with a seed of truth. There really was a strike at *The Day*, the Yiddish newspaper where my father wrote for years, and he went to work in a silversmith shop, the situation that informs "The Barking Dog." And he really did work briefly as a tutor/farmhand, the hook that gets "The Farmhand" going. As for "The Family Circle," there really was a Margoshes family circle, spearheaded by my mother, but beyond that, all three stories are fiction, as are all in the series, though some are more "fictional" than others.

As I continued to return to these stories, in between other writing projects, a few constants began to become clear to me. The most important was that, while the tone of the stories varies considerably, from sombre to comic, they're similar thematically in that they all show different glimpses of a fundamentally decent man in morally perplexing situations.

All the stories in the series walk that precarious tightrope between memoir and fiction. Of course, they're not true memoir – they're about my father, not me, though sometimes I appear briefly, as a child, listening to my father's tale. Sometimes I (the author) have myself (the character) ask a question or in some other way provide a foil for the character of my father. Mostly, though, the focus is on "my father," often in time periods before my birth. The stories are written in a blend of first and third person – when the character of myself as a child is on stage, it's first person; but when the focus is on "my father" alone, it's third. This bumping together of forms and techniques inevitably raises a question or two in the minds of some readers: is this truth or fiction, and how does the narrator know these things?

I worked hard, with the stories' structure and a sort of old-fashioned expository style, to make them *feel* like memoir – like truth – but, of course, most serious fiction writers do that all the time. We employ technique to garb our fabrications in an illusion of truth. We want the reader to buy into our fictions. I also worked hard to imbue these stories with a tension created by that unstated question of how the narrator came to know not just the stories, in their broad strokes, but the fine details.

Most importantly, I tried to honour my father. The best way to do that, I knew, was to get it right.

– Dave Margoshes

Acknowledgements

Most of the stories in this collection have appeared previously, sometimes in somewhat different versions, in literary magazines, in anthologies and in earlier collections.

* "A False Moustache" appeared in *Prism international*, 1985, and in *Small Regrets* (Thistledown Press, 1986).

* "Feathers and Blood" appeared in *Out of Place* (Coteau Books, 1991) and *Long Distance Calls* (Coteau Books, 1996).

* "A Book of Great Worth" appeared originally in *University of Windsor Review*, 1994, and subsequently in *Due West: Thirty Great Stories from Alberta, Saskatchewan and Manitoba* (NeWest/Coteau, Turnstone, 1996), *96: Best Canadian Stories* (Oberon Press, 1996) and *Long Distance Calls* (Coteau Books, 1996).

* "A Distant Relation" appeared in *Long Distance Calls* (Coteau Books, 1996).

* "Music by Rodgers, Lyrics by Hart" appeared in *Bix's Trumpet and other stories* (NeWest Press, 2007). Used with permission of the publisher.

* "*Lettres d'amour*" appeared in *Fiddlehead*, Spring 2008.

* "The Wisdom of Solomon" appeared in *The Dalhousie Review*, Autumn 2008, and subsequently in *The Journey Prize Stories 21* (McClelland & Stewart, 2009), and

online at www.theglobeandmail.com. It was a finalist for the 2009 Journey Prize.

* "The Barking Dog," "The Family Circle" and "The Farm Hand" appeared in *The New Quarterly*, Winter 2009.

A Book of Great Worth won the 2010 City of Regina Writing Award.

My thanks to the editors and jurors responsible, and special thanks to Thistledown Press and NeWest Press.

Thanks also to Geoffrey Ursell and Nik Burton for their belief in this project, and to Geoffrey for his sure editing hand.

About the Author

Dave Margoshes has published more than a dozen books of fiction, poetry, and nonfiction. His collection of stories, *Bix's Trumpet and Other Stories*, was Saskatchewan Book of the Year, won the Regina Book Award and was a finalist in the ReLit Awards in 2007. His three novels are *Drowning Man, I Am Frankie Stern*, and *We Who Seek: A Love Story*. He has published four other story collections, five volumes of poetry and several non-fiction works, including a biography of Tommy Douglas.

He has had stories and poems published in dozens of magazines and anthologies in Canada and the United States (including six times in *Best Canadian Stories*), had work broadcast on CBC, and given readings across the country. His awards include the Stephen

Leacock Prize for Poetry. He was also a finalist for the Journey Prize.

Some of his stories and poems spring from his days as an itinerant journalist. Margoshes worked for daily newspapers in eight cities, including San Francisco, New York, Calgary and Vancouver, covering everything from politics to murder to cat shows. He's also taught journalism. He currently lives near Saskatoon.

Berte and Harry Margoshes,
some time in the Nineteen Thirties

A Book of Great Worth is set in Adobe Caslon Pro.

William Caslon released his first typefaces in 1722. Caslon's types were based on seventeenth-century Dutch old style designs, which were then used extensively in England. Because of their remarkable practicality, Caslon's designs met with instant success. Caslon's types became popular throughout Europe and the American colonies; printer Benjamin Franklin hardly used any other typeface. The first printings of the American Declaration of Independence and the Constitution were set in Caslon.

For her Caslon revival, designer Carol Twombly studied specimen pages printed by William Caslon between 1734 and 1770. The OpenType "Pro" version merges formerly separate fonts (expert, swash, small caps, etc.), and adds both central European language support and several additional ligatures.

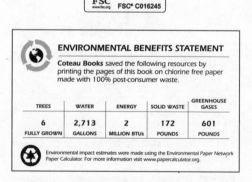

MIX
Paper from
responsible sources
FSC
www.fsc.org
FSC® C016245

ENVIRONMENTAL BENEFITS STATEMENT

Coteau Books saved the following resources by printing the pages of this book on chlorine free paper made with 100% post-consumer waste.

TREES	WATER	ENERGY	SOLID WASTE	GREENHOUSE GASES
6	2,713	2	172	601
FULLY GROWN	GALLONS	MILLION BTUs	POUNDS	POUNDS

Environmental impact estimates were made using the Environmental Paper Network Paper Calculator. For more information visit www.papercalculator.org.

Printed in Canada at Friesens